LEAD MINING IN THE PEAK DISTRICT

Compiled by members of the
Peak District Mines Historical Society and edited by
TREVOR D. FORD and J. H. RIEUWERTS

First Edition Published 1968
Reprinted with revisions 1970

SECOND EDITION : 1975
Reprinted 1981

PUBLISHED BY :
Peak Park Joint Planning Board :
Peak National Park Office, Baslow Road, Bakewell, Derbyshire, DE4 1AE
PEAK DISTRICT MINES HISTORICAL SOCIETY :
c/o Peak District Mining Museum, The Pavilion, Matlock Bath, Derbyshire
ISBN 0 901428 25 6

CONTENTS

PREFACE

This booklet has been compiled by members of the Peak District Mines Historical Society in the hope that visitors to the Peak District National Park will not only continue to admire its wonderful scenery, but also begin to take an interest in the many relics of one of Britain's erstwhile foremost industries. Lead mining formed the backbone of the wealth of the Peak District for over 1500 years. The limestone uplands and valleys, and parts of the marginal shale and gritstone country are littered with derelict shafts, grass covered spoil heaps and ruined buildings, forming conspicuous and characteristic features of many parts of the area.

Whilst industrial relics and beautiful scenery are not normally compatible, the old Derbyshire lead miners invariably used local materials for their buildings and shafts, and therefore they blend remarkably well with the surrounding countryside. The 'hillocks', or old spoil heaps of discarded stone and mineral from the workings are now largely grassed over, and could be passed by without a glance if attention were not drawn to them in the first place.

These remains are, however, rapidly disappearing, and the Peak District Mines Historical Society is making efforts in several directions in order to conserve the more important and interesting sites. The excursions in this booklet have been specially planned to illustrate the many facets of this ancient industry, and all contain important sites where preservation is desirable.

We would appeal, therefore, to the general public to assist wherever possible in this task. Please do not damage mining relics in any way, or throw stones into disused shafts, a practice which can dislodge the lining stones and thus render them unsafe. If a site becomes threatened by destruction, please contact the Society, who in turn may be able to either ensure preservation, or at the least obtain a photographic record and survey before all is lost forever.

Maps

The whole of the area described is shown on the 1:50000 Ordnance Survey Maps Sheets 199 (Buxton, Matlock and Dovedale) and 110 (Kinderscout and Castleton) and on the Peak District Tourist Map. For more detail the 1:25000 maps (2½ inches to 1 mile) maps will be useful. They are Sheets SK 05, SK 15, SK 16, SK 17, SK 18, SK 25, SK 26, SK 27, SK 35, SK 36.

The Geological Survey 1 inch: 1 mile maps 99 and 112 and the 1:25000 maps SK 17/18 (Edale and Castleton) and SK 25/26 (Matlock) add detail on the distribution of rock formations and minerals.

National Grid References are given throughout the text for easy location of places mentioned. The figures given in the margins of the sketch-maps are the 1 kilometre squares of the National Grid. All references fall within the 100 km. Square SK.

Rights of Way

Whilst most of the walks described herein are over public roads and footpaths, some of the mining relics are on private land and permission to visit them should be sought at the nearest farm. In any case visitors should observe the Countryside Code of good behaviour. Close gates, take home litter, be careful about fire dangers, and do not interfere with livestock, walls or farming equipment. Other routes described involve the use of cars. Drivers are requested to take care about parking, and not to block gates or narrow lanes.

Safety

On many of the old mining areas there are still open shafts, some unfenced. Take great care when walking through long grass that it does not conceal a shaft. Do not let children or pets play in such areas. Many old shafts are covered with a heap of stones which may collapse with little provocation. Make sure that heaps of stones are safe before climbing on them. Keep children away in any case—a loose stone can so easily cause a sprained ankle. Open mine entrances should only be entered with good reliable lighting. Do not let children go in with only a box of matches—there may be a concealed shaft in the floor! **Exploration of old workings is best undertaken in the company of experts.** Intending visitors should contact the Peak District Mines Historical Society for advice and assistance.

INTRODUCTION

Part One : The Lead Ores and Veins

The mineral veins of the Peak District are contained in the Carboniferous Limestone rocks and associated basalt lavas, and it is perhaps useful if these are described briefly first, before going into more detail on the veins and their minerals.

The limestones of the Peak District were formed as sediments on the floor of the sea in the Carboniferous period of geological time, roughly 330 million years ago, according to the latest estimates by geologists. The sea was clear and shallow and was inhabited by innumerable shell-fish, corals, sea-lilies and microscopic sea-weeds. When these died their remains accumulated as layer upon layer of shell debris which became hardened with time into limestone. It is these layers which now outcrop as the strata of the dale sides, and which were penetrated by the old miner in his search for lead ores. Around the fringes of the limestone area there were, at the time of sedimentation 330 million years ago, a series of reefs of coral and other limestones, so that in some ways the Derbyshire limestone area may be likened to a Pacific atoll today. These reefs of poorly stratified limestone outcrop at Castleton and in Dove Dale. As with some of the Pacific atolls today, the reefs and shallow seas of Carboniferous times had a scatter of small spluttering volcanoes, which poured out lava and ashes on to the sea floor from time to time. These are now seen as occasional dark bands along the dale sides, as for instance, near Ashford-in-the-Water, and Chee Dale.

The limestones varied somewhat in character; some were shell banks, others were coral-muds; and the old miner, as well as the modern geologist, had a variety of names for these varieties; "blackstone", "figured stone", "rosewood marble", etc. Perhaps these are easier to understand than the modern geologists' code of letters and numbers! The miner also had a variety of names for the lavas and ashes, such as "channel" and "cat-dirt", but all are collectively known as "toadstones". This name may be derived from "todt stein", the German for dead or unproductive stone since the lead veins are usually poor in minerals therein; or it may refer to its toad-like colouring of mottled green and brown; or it may be an expression of disgust when the miner encountered it . . . "t'owd . . . stone again"!

The study of the relations of the limestones, toadstones and veins provided an important part of the foundations of the science of geology in the late 18th century and early years of the 19th century, and names such as John Whitehurst, White Watson, John Farey, Elias Hall and William Martin, became internationally known through their inspired writings on the Derbyshire mines, strata and fossils. The lead ore of the Peak District is the common mineral galena, lead sulphide, and it is found in association with a variety of other minerals in veins of various types within the limestones and toadstones. To understand the nature of the mines and the reasons why certain mining practices were carried out, it is necessary to appreciate both the varied character of the veins, and the associations of minerals within them, and these may be classified into four types:

Rakes are the major veins running across country for a mile or more, consisting of minerals filling a fracture or fissure in the limestone which is usually nearly vertical. The fissure may be anything up to 20 feet in width, occasionally more, and many have been mined to depths of over 500 feet. None has ever been followed downwards

1

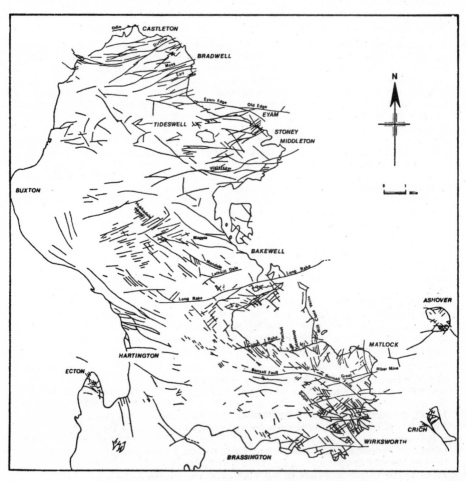

A Map of the mineral veins of the Peak District compiled by N. J. D. Butcher.

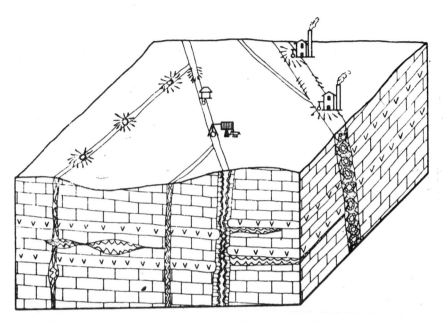

On the surface two parallel rakes are shown with scrins branching out of reach. The right-hand rake, worked by two Cornish Engines, has broken (brecciated) ore and gangue minerals. It is in a fault downthrowing the limestones with two included toadstone layers on the left. The left-hand rake has encrusted ore and gangue minerals, and has two flat veins spreading out to the right each capped by toadstones. The left-hand rake has been worked from a coe and from a horse-gin. The scrins to the left are linked by an irregular pipe-vein composed of mineral-lined caverns. There are hillocks and open climbing shafts on the left-hand scrin.

until it closed up, as water difficulties have interfered with deep mining. A rake thus consists of a nearly vertical wall of minerals up to 20 feet wide, 500 feet or more deep, and often a mile or more in length, with a few extending 4 or 5 miles. The obvious choice of mining methods has been by shafts spread out at intervals along the length, with accompanying hillocks of waste now demonstrating their position. From the shafts underground levels lead into stopes, cavities from which the mineral fill has been removed.

Scrins are minor equivalents of rakes. They are veins usually not more than a foot in width, and rarely coursing across country for more than a quarter of a mile or so. Workings do not often penetrate to depths greater than 200 ft. As with rakes, scrins are marked on the surface by lines of waste hillocks, and often with smaller shafts set closer together. Scrins are often found in swarms, which may branch out of rakes. A gradation in size between rakes and scrins means that the two terms are somewhat interchangeable when applied to veins of intermediate size.

3

Flats are mineral deposits lying more or less parallel to the stratification of the enclosing limestone, which is usually not far removed from the horizontal in Derbyshire. Flats have length and breadth more or less equal, up to ½ mile across, and their height (thickness) may be 20 feet or so. Examples are in the Golconda Mine at Brassington, on Masson Hill and on Bonsall Moor. They are often very irregular in shape. As their outcrop may often have been very limited, discovery was often by following a rake or scrin downwards by shafts. Levels were then driven out along the flats. Surface traces of old workings in flats look like an irregular variation of workings on a swarm of scrins.

Pipes are a variation of flats in which length greatly exceeds breadth, and again, there are intermediate deposits with interchangeable names. Pipes are not uncommon spreading out along the stratification of the enclosing limestone alongside rakes, so that only underground exploration of old shafts can reveal their presence. This feature is also apparent in old documents where a single vein may be referred to as either a rake or a pipe, e.g. Mandale Mine was in a rake with pipe-like extensions in the walls and the vein is variously recorded as Mandale Rake and Mandale Pipe. All four of these types of vein are found enclosed in the Carboniferous Limestone of the Peak District, which may be studied in the cliffs along many of the dales. These cliffs show to advantage many examples where the veins cut through the limestones, e.g. Lathkill Dale.

The minerals of the veins were formed by crystallization from solutions of hot fluids emanating from within the earth long after the formation of the limestones and toadstones. Both events may be dated by radio-active isotope methods. The age of the limestones and toadstones is about 330 million years, whilst the minerals arrived about 180 million years ago.

The mineralizing fluids flowed through the limestones cooling as they went, and deposited the minerals on the walls of the factures, or in ancient cave-systems, to form the veins. The toadstones, being relatively impervious, formed local barriers to flow and thus often controlled the disposition of veins. Rakes and scrins often closed up and lost their mineral content in toadstones though they might reappear in the limestones beneath, as in Seven Rakes Mine at Matlock, and in Millclose Mine. Flats and pipes often either lie on toadstone, or are roofed by a toadstone according to the prevalent direction of flow. Part of the limestone area was converted to the mineral dolomite, locally known as dunstone, which is much more porous, and some flats and pipes occur at the junction of the dolomite with the relatively impervious limestone, e.g. Portway Mine at Winster, Golconda Mine near Brassington and several on Masson Hill.

The lead mineral sought by the miners was galena, lead sulphide, which is easily recognizable by its silvery metallic lustre on a freshly broken surface. Few veins contained more than 10% of galena (which contains 86% lead metal) and then not consistently over a distance. An average yield was probably about 5%, though veins with as little as 2% seem to have been worked, probably at a loss, in the hope of the lead content improving further on. Associated with galena there is sphalerite, also known as blende or blackjack, actually zinc sulphide. This usually occurs in much smaller proportions, and if worked at all was generally only a by-product used as a source of zinc in brass-making.

In a few areas the lead and zinc sulphides have been oxidised to the carbonates, cerussite (lead carbonate) and smithsonite (zinc carbonate—commonly known as calamine). The former has been worked as white lead ore, used in paint, and the veins containing it were often known as White Rakes, e.g. at Brassington, Hucklow

4

Edge and at Wardlow. The latter has been worked also for paint manufacture, more commonly for brass-making and for medical purposes.

Production statistics are very incompletely recorded but a fair estimate is that between 2 and 3 million tons of lead ores have been recovered since mining began. Zinc ore production is much less and somewhere between $\frac{1}{4}$ and $\frac{1}{2}$ million tons would be a fair estimate.

Whilst the lead and zinc minerals have long been regarded as the ores, they are found with the associated gangue minerals, fluorspar, barytes and calcite. Forming more than 90% of most vein contents, these were regarded as waste, except for minor quantities of barytes used for paint manufacture, until late in the 19th century. If possible, these waste minerals were separated from the ore underground and were stacked in old workings as "deads". Nowadays the gangue minerals are the important product and the metal ores are simply by-products.

Fluorspar, calcium fluoride, is the chief source of fluorine compounds in chemical industry, of fluorine anaesthetics in medicine, of heat-resistant enamels, and is widely used as a flux in blast-furnace reduction of iron-ores. More than 200,000 tons is now produced annually in Derbyshire, and one mining company, Laporte Industries Ltd., operates two large fluorspar mines at Eyam.

Barytes, barium sulphate (strictly now called baryte, but commonly known in Derbyshire as "cawk") is now produced at about 40,000 tons per annum. It is used for paint manufacture, for glossy paper, toothpaste, as a source of barium in chemical industry, and in large quantities in oil or gas well drilling, in the North Sea, for example.

Two mines are working in a vein which is almost entirely calcite at Long Rake, near Youlgreave. The main demand for calcite (calcium carbonate—the same as limestone) depends on its consistent white colour, and it is used in terrazzo floor and wall surfacing. Other uses are in the mixture for white lines on roads, in stucco wall surfaces and other forms of ornamentation. It also finds uses in chemical industry.

Fluorspar is largely confined to a strip of the eastern margin of the limestone area about a mile wide, through Castleton, Bradwell, Hucklow, Eyam, Matlock and Wirksworth. It is generally a translucent white to cream colour, but may also occur in various shades of blue to purple. Freely grown crystals are cubic, but break with an oblique (octahedral) cleavage. Blue and white banded fluorspar occurs in the mines and caverns of Treak Cliff, Castleton and has been worked as Blue John for ornamental purposes since the mid 18th century. (*See Castleton itinerary*).

Barytes is an opaque cream colour, without an obvious crystalline form, often occurring in clusters of small imperfect crystals known as "cockscomb" habit. Its density distinguishes barytes easily, being half as heavy again as fluorspar, and nearly twice as heavy as an equivalent sized piece of calcite or limestone. It may occasionally occur in large white blade-like crystals, or with pink bands, or dark brown, looking like oak, e.g. oak-stone, the ornamental variety found near Arbor Low stone circle.

Calcite is found in many forms and in shades of white from chalky to glassy. Comb-structured calcite is the common form of many rakes, in parallel growths of turbid white to grey calcite. Nail-head spar is formed of stumpy hexagonal prisms, with flat rhombohedral terminations, common in association with Blue John or in hollow fossil shells. It is either clear or slightly creamy and translucent. Dog-tooth

5

spar is by far the commonest freely grown crystal form, and takes the form of sharp hexagonal pyramids, often intergrown, and sometimes with corroded or bevelled edges. Stalactites are also formed of calcite.

Intergrowths, or layered alternations of any of the above minerals are common.

Besides the above nearly a hundred other minerals have been recorded in the Peak District, but most are of academic significance only and are not common enough to be worked economically. Some are so rare that they are known from only a single locality and others were obtained from underground sites no longer accessible.

A full list, with annotations and references was given by T. D. Ford and W. A. S. Sarjeant in the Bulletin of the Peak District Mines Historical Society, Vol. 2, No. 3, 1964, which can be obtained through your public library.

Besides the above minerals a number of other materials have been mined in the Peak District. Perhaps the best known of these is the Ashford Black Marble, a very dark variety of limestone, which was mined near Ashford-in-the-Water in the 18th and 19th centuries. It takes a high polish and when inlaid with various coloured stones, including galena, fluorspar and barytes, was a highly favoured ornamental material for tables, mantel-pieces and other smaller articles. Two other varieties of limestone were also mined near Ashford, for use in inlay work. They were Rosewood Marble, mined in Nettler Dale, north of Sheldon, and Bird's Eye Marble, also found in Nettler Dale but quarried at the surface. The former was marked with irregular brownish laminations, which, when polished, looked like the veining in rose wood; the latter contained white fossil debris, largely of crinoid fragments in a nearly black matrix.

A brick-red iron-stained limestone was used for inlay and small ornamental work, e.g. the pulpit in Great Longstone Church, under the name of Duke's Red Marble. The Duke of Devonshire caused the whole deposit of this red limestone to be worked out when it was discovered in the walls of a vein in the Alport Mines about 1830, and the exact site is no longer known.

Various yellow, buff or red clays have been worked chiefly in the Brassington area, as ochre for use in colouring paint, etc. Manganese dioxide in the form of the black earthy "wad" has been obtained from a number of mines, chiefly Elton and Winster, again largely for use as a pigment.

Copper has been worked at Ecton in Staffordshire in a very extensive group of mines. The first records of working were in the mid 17th century but the peak period was the late 18th and 19th century. Judged from the available incomplete records some 4,000 tons of copper metal were obtained, in addition to unrecorded quantities of lead and zinc ores. Working ceased in the 1880s when the price of copper fell too low for economic extraction; but the deposits were never completely worked out. Specimens of chalcopyrite, malachite and azurite may still be found on the dumps.

Rottenstone was an incoherent porous weathering product of the black marble beds, worked for use as a mild abrasive, on the moors between Bakewell and Sheldon. Chert has long been mined at Bakewell, usually in large blocks used in grinding the china-clay mixture in the potteries of Staffordshire.

Limestone of the Hoptonwood Beds is being mined at present in the Middleton Limestone Mine at Middleton-by-Wirksworth. Some 5,000 tons of this high purity limestone are extracted every week for use in sugar-beet refining and the chemical industry.

INTRODUCTION

Part Two : History

EARLY HISTORY :

The origin of lead mining in the Peak District cannot be correctly ascertained by present day historians. Before the Roman occupation of this country, lead ore was obtained in the North Pennines, and it therefore seems likely, though not proven, that veins in the Peak District would be exploited at the same period.

The Romans definitely worked the ore and several 'pigs', or crude ingots of metallic lead, have been unearthed from time to time. The first was found about a foot beneath the surface on Cromford Nether Moor in the year 1777. Subsequently others have been found at Matlock Bank, Tansley Moor, and Bradwell; several others, although found outside the county, some as far away as Sussex, can be traced back to Derbyshire. At least 19 pigs are now known to have been cast in metal obtained from the Peak mines. Most of these have inscriptions on one or more faces and although drastically abbreviated, they usually permit the owner and place of manufacture to be deduced.

The Derbyshire pigs are distinguished by the letters LVT or LVTVD, or in one case LVTVDARES, all of which are believed to refer to *Lutudarum*. This is popularly supposed to have been located on the site of either Wirksworth or Matlock, but these suppositions are without direct evidence. Chesterfield, as a very ancient and well established lead market could be postulated, or the name may refer to the whole area of the mineral field.

A further difficult problem is presented by the letters EX ARG, and despite much speculation a wholly satisfactory translation and expansion does not appear to be available. Several translations seem possible and include, 'ex argento', meaning "made from silver"; 'ex argenteriis', "from the silver mines"; or 'ex argentiia officina', "from the silver refinery". Two of the pigs have pieces of galena embedded in them and it has been pointed out that galena could not have withstood the process of cupellation (the method of removing silver from lead), and remained unaltered. 'EX ARG' can also be taken to mean "that from which silver has been removed", but analyses have shown that the silver content of pigs is much the same as in galena. The Derbyshire ores are usually poor in silver content, and with the exception of the Ball Eye mine near Bonsall (285.574), they would not appear to be rich enough to be classed as silver ores. During the early years of the 18th century the latter mine is reputed to have produced an unusually large amount, so the foregoing interpretations of the inscriptions do not appear convincing unless they came either from Ball Eye Mine or a similar mine now lost. The Nestus Mine (292.585) on Masson Hill, Matlock, now the tourist attraction called Rutland Cavern, contains several rare copper and zinc minerals, and this area generally looks to be the likeliest site for a Roman silver mine, if indeed one ever existed.

Dating the pigs is also difficult and only the one from Cromford Moor can be dated accurately to the period AD 117-138.

So far as the actual sites of workings are concerned, most of the commercial show caverns at Matlock Bath claim to contain 'Roman galleries', and some written accounts quote descriptions of supposed Roman workings in Derbyshire mines.

These latter are of usually two quite distinct types, either very small square cut passages, generally two feet or less in width, and about three feet high, or the more common 'coffin' type levels so called because of their peculiar cross sectional shape. This latter type of level is generally higher, generally four to five feet, and up to several hundred feet in length.

Good examples of the square cut type of passage can be seen in the Masson Mine at Matlock, in a mine near Wirksworth, and in the Whalf-Hillocks Mine (146.672) near Monyash. They are generally driven in barren limestone as cross cuts linking workings, rather than along the line of a mineral vein itself.

Without the aid of documentary evidence, these old levels are impossible to date, but comparison with adjacent workings, their range and position, coupled with appearance, invariably gives the impression of great age. Whether by this one means Roman, Saxon, Mediaeval or later it is impossible to say.

The 'coffin levels' are more abundant and many have been regarded as being of Roman origin. However recent documentary evidence has shown that some of these levels were made as late as the mid 18th century, and almost all the known 'coffin levels' in Derbyshire can be dated to the 17th century or later.

The extraction of the lead ore by the Romans would probably be mainly confined to the open workings along the outcrops of the major veins. Sometimes the veins could be between 40 and 60 feet wide at the surface, and whilst this was not exclusively filled with lead ore, the workings could be taken to a fair depth by opencast methods. Undoubtedly the Romans possessed the knowledge and technical skill required to undertake deep mining, but open-cast working would be a far more economical proposition, and the large veins easily worked at surface would provide ample employment without recourse to driving levels in the relatively hard limestone.

There are a limited number of mines with workings apparently of great antiquity, but, because of lack of any documentary evidence, they cannot be dated. The Nestus Mine is a good example, as there are workings which had their mineral ores extracted many centuries ago.

After the withdrawal of the Roman forces, there was a lapse of some 600 years before the Norman Conquest. During the intervening period both the Saxons and the Danes filtered into the Peakland hills and continued mining, but it is thought on a smaller scale than previously.

In the 9th century the mines at Wirksworth were attached to the Abbey of Repton, and were evidently of considerable importance because lead worth 300 shillings had to be paid as annual rent charge to Christ Church, Canterbury. The Danish army destroyed Repton Abbey in 874 and the Manor of Wirksworth along with the lead mines passed into the hands of the Danish King Ceolwulf. The mines at this date became the property of the Crown, and the mineral dues in the 'King's Field' now belong to the Duchy of Lancaster. The King's Field does not cover the entire mining field, and the owners of the different Mining Liberties will be discussed later.

The Odin Mine (134.834) near Castleton, traditionally derives its name from being worked at the time of the Danes.

The Domesday Survey, undertaken in 1086, lists 7 lead works. In this context "works" may mean smelters, rather than mines, and each smelter would serve a number of mines. One works was at each of Bakewell, Ashford, Crich and Matlock, and three were at Wirksworth. Soon afterwards the mines were leased to William

Peveril, the illegitimate son of William the Conqueror, and during the twelfth century mines were being worked at Bakewell, Wardlow, Tideswell and Wirksworth. Sometime in this century William Peveril was disgraced, dispossessed of his rights and the mines reverted to the Crown.

ORIGIN AND EARLY DEVELOPMENT OF MINING CUSTOMS :

Until the end of the 13th century the Derbyshire miners' right to dig for lead ore was merely based on customs and privileges handed down from 'time immemorial'. The miners therefore petitioned King Edward I in 1287 to set down their customs and rights. This petition had resulted largely because they had recently been met with several actions for trespass from the landowners. Edward I ordered that an Inquisition be held at Ashbourne on the Saturday after Trinity Sunday, 1288, to enquire into the miners' claims. At this Inquisition the laws were set down for the first time and they formed the nucleus of the Derbyshire lead mining laws for the next six centuries.

At this point it may help if the broad outlines of the mining laws, not only the ones set down in 1288, but some important subsequent ones, are outlined. Within the King's Field any man could search for lead ore without hindrance from the land-owner, only certain places being exempted from this peculiar custom. Churchyards, gardens, orchards and the high-way could not be disturbed in the search for ore, although lead was worked from beneath such places on many occasions.

A vein, when first discovered, had to be 'freed', that is application had to be made to the Barmaster, (a Crown official who deals with all lead mining queries and customs), to register the name of the new vein in his book; at the same time one 'freeing dish' of ore being paid to him by the miners. These dishes represented the initial payment due to the owners of the mineral duties.

The volume of the Standard Dish is 14 Winchester pints and the original Dish presented to the miners by Henry VIII in 1513 is still preserved in the Moot Hall at Wirksworth. It holds about 65 lbs. of lead ore.

The Barmaster, upon receipt of this freeing dish allowed the finders of the new vein two 'Founder Meers' of ground. The meer, which is a very ancient unit, is 32 yards in length in the High Peak irrespective of the width or depth of the vein. The length of the meer varies in different parts of the mining area; some localities, for example, Ashford Southside Liberty had 29 yards to the meer, whilst in Youlgreave Liberty it was only 28 yards.

The payment of the freeing dish to the Barmaster enabled the miners to work for a distance of two meers in their new vein, and as deep as their resources would allow, the width of the working being governed by the width of the vein itself. The third meer was called the Lord's Meer and belonged exclusively to the owner of the mineral duties. Since the year 1690, the mineral duties in the High Peak have been leased from the Duchy of Lancaster by the Dukes of Devonshire. The laws and customs applicable to the King's Field do not necessarily apply elsewhere. For example the Liberties of Bakewell, Harthill (formerly known as Hartle) Haddon and Hazelbadge are the mineral property of the Duke of Rutlands and do not belong to the Crown. Miners in these liberties did not have identical laws with those of the King's Field, but broadly speaking they were similar. There are other liberties belonging to private individuals, which again are quite separate from any of the above.

9

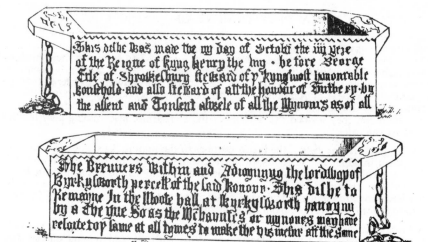

The inscription reads:-

"This dish was made the iiij day of October iiij year of the reigne of Kyng Henry viij (1513) before George Erle of Shrowesbury Steward of the Kyngs most honourable household and allso Steward of all the honour of Tutbery by the assent and consent as well of all the Mynours as of all the Brenners within and adjoining the Lordship of Wyrkysworth Percell of the said honour This dishe to Remayne In the Moote Hall at Wyrkysworth hanging by a cheyne so as the Merchauntes or Mynours may have resorte to the same at all times to make the trew mesure at the same".

The third meer, or Lord's Meer, could either be bought by the miners, or they had a right to work through it, but in this latter case could not sell any ore they obtained in so doing. If they decided to purchase the Lord's Meer outright, then the Barmaster and members of the Barmoot Court were called to descend the mine, view the vein, and place a valuation on it. The Barmoot Court is still held and although today its function is somewhat traditional, in the mining days there was generally a great deal of work to be transacted and the jurymen, who were miners or had connections with the industry, dealt with disputes of ownership, non-payment of debts, and other mining and mineral matters. After the miners had worked, or worked through, the Lord's Meer, they could free as many subsequent Taker meers as they wished. These had to be kept at work otherwise they could be 'nicked' or counterclaimed by other miners wishing to work the vein. Providing that the vein was worked to the satisfaction of the Barmaster it could not be forfeited. Should the vein stand idle through lack of adequate ventilation, or because it was drowned with water, then it could not be 'nicked' or forfeited.

10

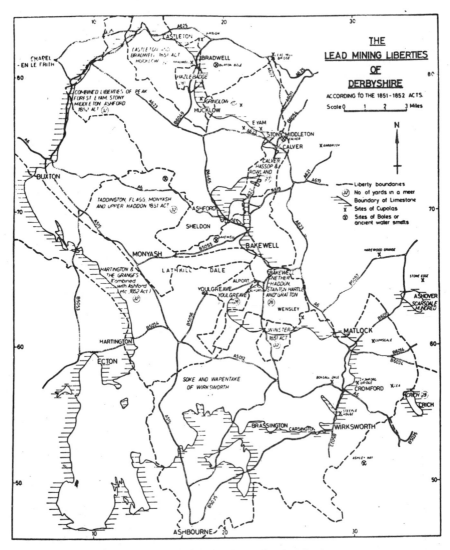

A map of the Lead Mining Liberties of the Peak District.

In addition to the 'freeing dishes' paid by the miners to the owners of the mineral duties, other Royalties were also payable. These included both 'Lot' and 'Cope' and also Tithe. It is impossible to explain in detail all the ramifications of the Derbyshire mining laws and customs, and, as already explained, they differ from one locality to another. Briefly, the Lot was taken as a certain fraction of the dressed ore. Normally this amount was 1/13th, but at times this was altered by the Mineral Lords, sometimes on account of the low price of lead which made mining less profitable than usual. The Cope was generally paid by the lead merchants and was in places 4d. per load, in others 6d. per load. The Cope was taken as payment in lieu of the Mineral Lord having first right to purchase the ore. Sometimes this Cope payment was rented out to one of the Barmasters. Nine dishes were reckoned to equal one load, and the load varied in weight, dependent on the quality of the ore, so that about 3½ to 4 loads would be equal to 1 ton.

It was at the Inquisition of 1288 where the framework of these curious and ancient laws was set out. They may have been derived in the first place largely from the Saxons. After many additions and modifications, the laws were finally passed as two Acts of Parliament, one in 1851 for the High Peak, the other in 1852 for the Soke and Wapentake of Wirksworth, the combined Liberties of Eyam and Stoney Middleton, Tideswell, Ashford and Hartington and the Liberty of Crich.

More detailed accounts of the laws will be found by consulting the Bibliography, but possibly the most entertaining way to read them is to consult the 'Rhymed Chronicle' of Edward Manlove, first published in 1653. Manlove was Steward of the Wirksworth Barmote Court, and he set down in verse the quaint customs with which he would be obviously very familiar.

MINING METHODS.

ORE AND ROCK EXTRACTION :

The process of ore extraction was very crude even into the early years of the 18th century. Several methods were employed for the actual extraction of the rock and ore, and this largely depended on the nature of the material to be dug out. The earliest method was undoubtedly that of working opencast along the line of the outcrop of the vein, but trenches cut in the vein could not be of any depth because of the instability of the walls. Shallow shafts were sometimes sunk and short tunnels driven out from the foot. These were rarely of any considerable length, bad ventilation usually being the limiting factor, so another shaft was sunk close by and the process repeated. Very old workings along the veins were characterised by the exceptionally close pitting of the shafts. Many veins in Derbyshire show this feature, particularly fine examples are to be seen on the Bonsall Leys veins, west of Slaley, on Bonsall Moor. Later, as methods of ventilation and drainage improved, deeper and longer levels became possible, but the actual breaking down of the rock presented a problem. A pick having one end pointed and the other end blunted like a hammer head was often used. The pointed end could be inserted into any small crack or opening, and the other end struck by a heavy hammer. This was quite an effective way of breaking down vein stuff, and also rock, if it was well bedded or jointed. Wedges were also used and after a small crack had been opened a little with a pick, wedges were driven in and a series of heavy blows would be capable of breaking off large pieces of rock. A later development of this process became known as 'plug and feathers'. Two plates of iron were placed in a crevice, and a wedge of iron driven between them. With the use of several sets, rock could be broken down in a reasonably effective way.

Early mining by shallow shafts and short galleries as shown in Agricola's "De Re Metallica" 1556.

13

Before the introduction of gunpowder, sometime in the last quarter of the 17th century, two other methods of rock and ore excavation to be used were those of 'fire setting' and 'lime blasting', both being utilised in Derbyshire. The former consisted of a fire being lit against the rock face, causing it to become extremely hot. Water was then douched onto it, resulting in cracking and fragmentation. The face could then be easily worked. There is record of an unlit fire having been found in an old working near Taddington, and workings on the Coal Pit Rake (289.583) at Matlock Bath shows signs of fire setting. By mineral law, fires were only to be lit after 4 p.m., this being an obvious safeguard against suffocation. The process of lime blasting was totally different. A hole was bored in the limestone and into this was placed a quantity of quicklime. A wooden bung was plugged into the drill hole, water then being poured through a small hole in the bung itself. The action of the water on the quicklime is very intense. The quicklime is converted into slaked lime with expansion and the generation of great heat. This violent chemical reaction is sufficient to split the rock. The Ball Eye Sough, an old drainage level near Cromford, is considered in part at least to have been made by lime blasting.

EARLY DRAINAGE TECHNIQUES :

Two other problems concern the early techniques of lead ore extraction, namely, ventilation and drainage. Both were considerable obstacles to the driving of long levels and the sinking of deep workings. By the 17th century the workings along the lead veins were generally approaching the water table. This is usually determined by the contour of the nearest valley floor, but there may be local irregularities due to impervious layers of igneous rock or other geological complications. Above the water table, the mines were tolerably dry, but below this level the miners were quite often in serious difficulties with large volumes of water. Anyone who has explored old lead mines in the limestone in Derbyshire will appreciate that considerable seepage takes place through the upper workings, and although these may be 200 ft. to 300 ft. or more above the local water table, they can be uncomfortably wet. Before the 17th century various types of pumps were in use. One of the earliest methods employed was that of winding water in leather buckets by means of a windlass. Wherever possible water was run off into natural cavities underground, the alternative being to wind it all the way to the surface, or if a small tunnel conveniently led to a nearby valley this could save some winding distance. Because of the cavernous nature of the limestone, natural cavities or 'self-opens' as the old miners called them were sometimes utilised for the drainage of the mine water. Later, many drainage levels were driven to these caves and underground river courses, this saving the miners the trouble of driving a level all the way to the nearest valley side.

An improvement on the leather bucket system was known as the 'Chain pump'. The buckets were attached to an endless chain, with a toothed wheel of two or three feet diameter situated at the top of the pump barrel. The wheel was turned by a hand-operated windlass, and the chain descended outside the barrel, ascending on the inside. The water was discharged into wooden troughs or 'trogues', at the top of the barrel. The barrels or cylinders were normally made of wood, possibly merely a hollowed out tree trunk, and were bound with iron hoops. There were many variations of these pumps, some being worked by water-wheels geared to the wheel round which the chain passed; others were worked by horses. A Rag and Chain pump was slightly different. Here the barrel was about 20 feet long and the endless chain had great knobs of leather or rag or even both stuck on to iron spikes. The chain and the knobs fitted tightly inside the cylinder or barrel.

Georgius Agricola's wonderful work 'De Re Metallica' published in 1556, contains many drawings of early mining apparatus including pumping machinery. Agricola obtained this information from German mining areas, but Derbyshire was soon under the influence of this technology because German miners and engineers came to the county during the 16th century. There is evidence that a horse whim, driving a rag and chain pump, was still in use at the Goodluck Mine near Wirksworth in the 19th century.

DEVELOPMENT IN DRAINAGE :

SOUGHS OR LEVELS IN THE 17th CENTURY

By the beginning of the 17th century most of the larger lead veins in the Peak District had been worked down to, or were rapidly approaching, the water table. The driving of soughs from a lower contour in an adjacent valley, or from a deeper valley, which could be two or three miles away from the mines, enabled the water table to be lowered still further. These soughs were to become very much the symbol of the Derbyshire lead miner's skill, perseverance and endurance. Today some of these soughs, although driven between 250 and 300 years ago, are still in good condition. Modern miners and explorers of the old lead mines, both speak in awe at the workmanship in these long levels.

The first sough for which documentary evidence is available is the one commenced about 1632 by the Dutch drainage expert Sir Cornelius Vermuyden. He had originally come to this country at the invitation of King Charles I to direct the drainage of the Fenlands and to reclaim land in the Isle of Axholme, Lincolnshire. Subsequently, he became interested in the Dove Gang Lead mines between Cromford and Wirksworth. These mines were exceedingly rich but had already been worked down to the water table. The sough was completed as far as the Gang Vein by 1651 and the driving of the level enabled the mine to be worked for many years before the deeper Cromford Sough was driven. Bates or Longhead Sough (293.564) was driven sometime after 1651, but before Cromford Sough was begun, to unwater the Godbehere Vein, virtually an eastward extension of the Gang Vein beneath Black Rocks.

Cromford Sough was probably started in 1672 and its tail or outlet is still visible behind the houses near Cromford Market Place (295.567). Part of it has been explored in modern times. It was driven through limestone and shale to Godbehere Vein and the Gang Vein, although several other veins had been unwatered before these veins were reached. The sough was extended at various periods and branch levels driven from it; by the later 18th Century it extended in one direction almost to Wirksworth.

Other large soughs under construction at this time were the Hannage Sough, commenced about 1793 at Willowbath Mill and driven to the mines north of Wirksworth; the Maury Sough near Taddington; the Winster Sough draining the Portaway Pipe and the sough started in 1663 or just before to take water from the old and rich Odin Vein, near Castleton.

VENTILATION :

Ventilation was the second major problem confronting the miners, and in conjunction with the water hazard, it persisted until the last part of the 19th century. The working levels became deeper, and the exploratory cross-cuts and the soughs became longer, both needing better and more efficient means of bringing fresh air to the 'forefield' or working face. Some of the soughs were driven through shale, and the deadly firedamp and other gases given off by this formation made the problem more acute. It is said that when the Cromford Sough was being made, baskets containing red hot coals were lowered into shafts sunk along the line of the level, in an attempt to obtain a circulation of fresh air. This practice was resorted to more frequently in coal mining. The more usual mode of ventilation was to force a blast of fresh air to the fore-field utilising metal or wooden pipes encased in clay. Bellows, powered either by hand, or by a water wheel whenever possible, blew a constant stream of fresh air into the pipes. There is a reference in an early 19th century reckoning book to a 'vintilator' being used at the Mandale Mine (195.661) in Lathkill Dale, but there is no indication as to what type of machine this was, or how it operated, but it is interesting to note that the same book records payments for metal pipes for the mine.

PREPARATION OF ORE READY FOR SMELTING :

Once above ground, the ore had to be dressed before being smelted. The lead ore was known under different names as it passed through the various dressing processes, before being smelted in the furnace. When raised from the mine, the ore was known as 'fell' or 'bouse' and this was initially sorted on the 'bank' or 'striking floor'. Rich pieces, known as 'bing' were taken immediately to the ore house or 'bingstead'. The remainder was dressed, generally by women or boys, using hammers called 'buckers', and was crushed to about the size of peas. This was then sieved in a vat of water. The sieve was immersed in the vat and at the same time agitated. During this operation the lighter rock and gangue minerals are partially separated from the heavier lead ore, and are skimmed off and thrown on the hillock. Large pieces of ore were hand picked and taken to the ore house. The size of the sieves varied, being sometimes ⅜ inch diameter mesh, and sometimes ¼ inch. This ore was known as 'peasy ore' and the material passing through the sieves, 'smitham' or 'offal'. The final stage of the dressing room was known as 'buddling' and this operation consisted of the remaining ore and sludge being washed over an inclined elongated trough. The material was raked across a stream of water, and the lighter rock and minerals particles remained at the top while the heavier lead fines were deposited at the bottom of the buddle by the action of gravity. The smallest kind of lead ore was called 'belland' and some fields near to lead dressing floors and smelting sites are still today known as 'Belland field'. Sometimes old miners or more particularly women, would rewash the old hillocks for the small quantity of lead left by the former miners.

The introduction of the sieve into Derbyshire is usually attributed to one William Humphray in the year 1565, but at the same time it was counterclaimed that in fact Burchard Kranich had already used the method about 1530 and that upwards of 2,000 poor people had made their livelihood by sieving on the old hillocks. The buddle was also reputedly introduced into the county at about the same period. Previously a good deal of the fine ore had been discarded, having only been dressed by hammers, so this would explain why so many people found it profitable to rework the old hillocks. Strawberry Rake, lying south of Coombs Dale, and associated with the large veins known as Deep Rake, was the scene of some of these very early reworkings of old hillocks.

"Buddling" lead ore as shown by Agricola in 1556.

17

JIGGING MACHINE

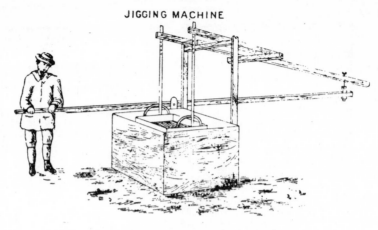

JIGGING MACHINE

BUDDLING

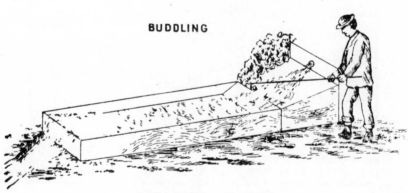

Jigging and budding ore (from Stokes).

LEAD SMELTING PRIOR TO 1700 :

The techniques employed in the actual smelting of the lead ore also advanced during this time, again as a result of work done by William Humphray, although Burchard claimed that he had used Humphray's methods some time previously. The ancient manner of smelting had been done by 'Boles', sited on west-facing hilltops to take advantage of the prevailing wind in forcing a draught. These smelting places were extremely crude and consisted merely of a low wall of stones, a few feet in diameter, with an opening facing the wind. A channel led from the interior of the bole to a small basin into which ran the melted lead. The ore was placed on a layer of wood followed by further layers of wood and ore repeated several times. If the wind was strong enough, at least a partial smelting of the ore resulted, and a pig of lead could be cast. The slags, which contained a recoverable percentage of lead, were re-smelted using charcoal as an additional fuel to the wood in order to obtain the requisite higher temperature. These slags were called 'black slags'. The map of Derbyshire and the adjacent South Yorkshire hills are dotted with 'Bole Hills', each marking the site of a former smelting hearth, although caution must be exercised in the interpretation of the meaning of some of the Sheffield area Bole Hills, as some undoubtedly refer to ironstone smelting sites.

The first major change in smelting methods came in the mid 16th century with the introduction of the true furnace. William Humphray was granted Letters Patent in 1565 for smelting lead ore with a furnace blown by bellows. He subsequently built a smelting mill on the River Sheaf at Beauchief, south of Sheffield, and leased some lead mines near Calver. Humphray claimed that Burchard had infringed his rights, but it is clear that although Burchard had made lead in 1552-53, with a furnace which used a water wheel to work the bellows, it was different in its design from Humphray's furnace. The Burchard furnace was situated at Duffield. A commission established to investigate the claims of both men described Humphray's furnace as having a 'workstone' and the ore being stirred by workmen during the process. In 1581 it was noted that Humphray's was a continuous process. Whilst Burchard probably introduced a water blown bellows furnace before Humphray, the latter's furnace was obviously quite different, and it is evident that the construction and mode of operation were also different. Nearly one hundred and eighty years were to pass before the introduction of a new type of smelting furnace.

THE 'HEYDAY' OF LEAD MINING : THE YEARS 1700 - 1750 :

The opening of the 18th century proved to be the dawn of a particularly active period, and during the next 190 years saw the industry rise to a peak of technological advance, and a zenith of ore production. It witnessed also the beginning of the decline which was to terminate in the mid 20th century, with the ultimate closing of virtually all mines as purely lead producers, and the parallel growth from about 1900 of the fluorspar industry. The 18th century saw the introduction of the steam engine as a motive power for pumping in the Peak lead mines, the driving of the major sough, and later, of the first signs of capitalised mining in the district.

A very limited amount of capital had been available in the 17th century and wealthy London merchants and local lead merchants and smelters became partners in mines without apparently encouraging any technological advances. They provided a certain proportion of the finance for the day to day working of the mines, which perhaps may have been difficult for the working miner/shareholder to contribute on his own.

19

The early years were characterised by the discovery of extensions of several old and well tried veins. The Hucklow Edge Vein had been worked during the 17th century west of the village of Great Hucklow. A bed of toadstone outcrops west of Tideslow· Top and dips away eastwards. The mines were only worked in the overlying limestone and therefore became successively deeper as the vein approached the village of Great Hucklow. Not until the 1760's was an attempt made to sink through this bed of toadstone and work the vein in the limestone beneath. The vein was also very 'shackey' or cavernous and in the latter half of the 17th century drainage levels had been driven and their water turned underground into these 'Shacks' or 'self opens' as the old miners termed them. At Great Hucklow, the vein disappears beneath the overlying Edale Shales, and this covering becomes progressively thicker as the vein ranges eastwards under Eyam Edge, until at the Ladywash mine, north of Eyam village, a total thickness of 796 feet of shales and gritstone had to be sunk through before the underlying limestone was reached.

About 1711, it was realised that this large vein was ranging in a general eastwardly direction, running approximately parallel with the scarp face of Eyam Edge. Almost simultaneously several mines, amongst them, Little Pasture, Haycliffe, and Middleton Engine, all of which had previously worked other veins lying south of the Hucklow Edge vein, began cutting shale-gates northwardly to locate the extension of the main vein, which they presumed would range across the northern end of their ground. These shale-gates not only acted as trial levels, but later when signs of the vein had been seen in the shale, and shafts had been sunk down to the actual vein itself, they acted as drainage levels and were titled soughs on mining plans. They were, in actual fact, not true soughs, but pumpways, not being deep enough to intersect the vein, but at the same time saved 200 or 300 feet of laborious hand pumping all the way to the surface. The main engine shafts of the Eyam Edge mines were generally between 400 and 1,000 feet deep.

The vein was extremely rich and ore worth many thousands of pounds was raised annually from its mines. Disputes regarding ownership of parts of the vein between neighbouring mines were fairly common, and one such dispute between the partners of the Little Pasture mine and the Miners Engine mine (205.775) lasted for over 50 years without being successfully resolved. The trouble started in the 1730's and developed because of the discovery of a branch vein, to which each mine claimed title. Adding to the confusion was the fact that it was not altogether clear at the time which of the two veins was the continuation of the Hucklow Edge vein. Due largely to the complex mineral laws, extended litigation followed, which passed from the hands of the Barmaster and the Barmote Court into the Court of Chancery. The argument was still not settled in 1792, although the Barmote Court had meanwhile decided that the more northerly of the two veins was the Hucklow Edge Vein, this ranging through the Broadlow (211.777) and Ladywash mines (220.777) whilst the other vein ranged nearly south east towards Shaw Engine mine (222.771) and became known as the Old Edge Vein.

The Odin Vein near Castleton, was in a similar geological position to the Hucklow Edge Vein, in that it was initially exploited in the limestone and was later followed beneath the capping of Edale Shales. By 1663 drainage problems had been encountered and a sough level was made at the eastern end of the vein which provided drainage from the old workings. These workings were, in all probability, situated where the now familiar Odin Gorge can be seen on the south side of the Castleton - Chapel-en-le-Frith road, at the foot of Mam Tor. This old level probably had·its entrance about 80 yards north of Knowlegates Farm and was driven through the toe of the Mam Tor landslip and Edale Shales to the working beneath Odin Gorge. This sough is interesting in that it is one of the earliest recorded Derbyshire drainage levels. During the first half of the 18th century the vein was worked progressively further west under the south eastern flank of Mam Tor. Natural caverns were intersected, and in times of flood great volumes of water flowed into the mine via these caverns. Their position, deep beneath the shale of Mam Tor, is geologically interesting. The mine nevertheless proved to be very rich and large profits are recorded in the mine reckoning books.

Watergrove Mine (188.758) near Foolow, was another mine to be worked in the first half of the century; by 1740 no less than three soughs had been started in an attempt to alleviate the water problem. Two of them did not ultimately extend for any distance and did not help in the eventual draining of the mine. The main drainage level, Watergrove Sough (212.757) did not reach the mine until 1805, and during the intermediate period two pumping engines had been erected. The first of them was in use by 1748 and by the end of the century, another had been put to work. The latter was a Newcomen engine, had a 40 inch cylinder, a 7 ft. stroke and pumps of 16 inch diameter. It was put up for sale with other mining plant when the mine was abandoned in 1853.

The area also had several other early soughs, which besides the one driven to Watergrove already mentioned, included the Stoke Sough (240.766) begun about 1724 from the side of the River Derwent, north of Stoke Hall. This one was of the first major soughs in Derbyshire, being intended to drain the Eyam Edge mines at a much deeper level than the earlier shale gate soughs, previously discussed, and which only served individual mines. Men were killed by explosions of firedamp during the making of Stoke Sough, and rock-oil was found in nodules in the shale. The miners used this oil in the first place for greasing their boots, but found that it shrivelled the leather, so afterwards the oil was used to provide illumination for the mining operations.

The Magclough Sough (237.775) was another drainage level, driven in the 1720s and 1730s in opposition to the Stoke Sough, to provide deep level drainage for the Eyam Edge mines.

Explosions of a more spectacular kind occurred in the Haycliffe mine (214.773), situated on the lower slopes of Eyam Edge north west of the village. The vein in this mine was 'slickensided', i.e. its walls had been fluted and polished by the movement of rocks in opposition to each other during earth movements. Occasionally the stresses produced during the movements remained unrelieved and when struck with a miner's pick the adjacent minerals exploded with great violence.

In Haycliffe Mine such surfaces were coated with a film of galena and were polished like a mirror. One writer, in describing an explosion in 1738, recorded that over 30 tons of rocks were blown down by the blast. On other occasions men were injured, but often creakings were heard beforehand and gave the miners a chance to run clear. Theories offering possible explanations for this curious phenomenon include ignition of firedamp by a spark from a pick striking the rock; a sudden release of stresses within the vein-stuff caused by the removal of the adjacent rock; and chemical reactions taking place, particularly when the vein minerals are freshly exposed. The explosions have also occurred in the Odin Mine, Castleton, in the Gang Mine on Cromford Moor; in Cockersfield Vein, near Great Hucklow and in the Clayton Adit at the Ecton copper mines.

21

THE IMPACT OF THE INDUSTRIAL REVOLUTION ON LEAD MINING, PUMPING MACHINERY AND CAPITAL MINES :

The introduction of the steam engine into Derbyshire lead mining was a tremendous advance in the problems of draining the mines. The laborious and largely ineffective methods of hand pumping and associated ideas previously employed have already been outlined. Certainly the construction of the soughs alleviated drainage troubles, but the new ideas were slow to penetrate. Probably the main reason for this was simply that many of the Derbyshire mines were small, often worked by the Shareholders themselves and with certain notable exceptions continued to be so even into this century.

Gradually, capitalists in the form of lead merchants, smelters, landed gentry and others began to invest in the mines on a larger scale than ever before, but many workings all over the mining field continued to be wrought only on a part time basis by the farmer/lead miner. These small concerns did not have the capital to buy costly pumping machinery, and many rich mines, worked to the water table and possibly a little deeper by means of small pumps discharging into soughs, had to be abandoned until partnerships with the necessary capital could install costly pumping machinery.

Capital mines opened in the 19th century, equipped with pumping engines of varying types, worked side by side with small mines operated in the most primitive ways. A. H. Stokes, the Inspector of Mines for the area, writing in 1880, stated that he believed some mines were then utilising methods little better than the Saxon mode of mining. This is an exaggeration, but it vividly illustrates the poverty under which some mines worked.

The first steam engine to be erected on a Derbyshire lead mine was at the Yatestoop mine at Winster in 1715, only three years after the first ever Newcomen engine had been erected on a Midlands coal mine in 1712. Farey, writing in 1811, observed that a total of 5 engines had been working on the Yatestoop mine and 6 at other mines near Winster. The Rev. Clegg touring Winster in 1730 noted three steam engines at work and was most impressed by them. All these engines were of the Newcomen type. The mines around Winster and Elton were very rich. They attracted the attention of the London Lead Company in 1720; this company carried out a considerable amount of work, initially to mines situated on Bank Pasture (245.605) east of Winster, and subsequently extended their activities to mines situated between there and Wensley, and later to mines elsewhere in the county. The company did not expend as much energy on their Derbyshire mines as they did on their properties in the Northern Pennines, nevertheless they erected a Newcomen engine made by Abraham Darby at Coalbrookdale Ironworks on the Mill Close Vein in 1748, and were responsible for the driving of a sough to the Bank Pasture mines. They were also directly involved in the introduction of a new type of smelting furnace. This became known as the Low Arched Reverbatory Furnace or Cupola, the first being erected at Ashover in 1735. The Cupola was a totally different type of furnace from anything previously used. The ore was not in direct contact with the fuel, and the flames from the burning coal were drawn over the ore by means of a draught induced by a long flue and chimney. Furnaces of this type were later built at Totley, near Sheffield; Harewood on Beeley Moor (3068); Lumbs, between Matlock and Tansley; Rowsley and elsewhere and the older smelting mills much as those at Shacklow Wood on the River Wye and the mills at Calver and Stoke on the River Derwent fell into disuse. The remains of the long flues of one smelting mill can still be seen on the east side of Bradwell Dale, and are virtually all that remain of this once well known site.

22

The Cowclose and Leadnams Mines, near Elton, were also very rich. For example, in a period of 10 years lead ore to the value of £23,000 was mined, and a steam pumping engine was erected on the Cowclose Mine in 1755. A great deal of activity was similarly focussed on the mines lying south of the River Lathkill, near Alport. Several soughs had been driven to this rich complex of veins during the latter years of the 17th century and the early years of the 18th century. The Stanton Sough (245.643) was driven through the shale approximately parallel to, and south of Lathkill, in order to relieve the Bowers Rake; while Rainstor Sough (237.652) was driven to veins on the north side of the same river. Alport Sough (227.648), begun in 1706, and the Blythe Sough (231.643) were other shallow levels, both of which enabled vast quantities of lead to be raised.

However, in 1766, a large, low level sough called Hill Carr Sough, or sometimes Stanton Moor Sough, was begun from the side of the River Derwent (259.634) to give deeper drainage to the Alport mines. The making of this long sough proved to be an immense undertaking. The rock was of such extreme hardness that drills suitable for boring the shot holes were difficult to obtain. The black blasting powder had to be sealed in containers to prevent moisture getting to it, and much trouble was experienced providing adequate ventilation for the sough forefield. Not until 1783 was the Guy Vein reached. The sough had several branches and boats were used to bring out the waste rock.

The men who undertook to drive the long soughs were generally capitalists with large sums of ready money to invest. Sometimes they were partners in mines and sometimes they were lead smelters or merchants. The Alsop family had shares in numerous lead mining ventures including Hill Carr Sough. The Nightingales, Barkers, Wilkinsons and Nodder families all had extensive shares in Derbyshire lead mines and there were many more. Before a sough was made, the usual procedure was to draw up a legal agreement between the soughmasters or 'undertakers' and the proprietors of the mines to be "unwatered". Usually marks were made in the mines at the standing water level, and the soughmasters received a certain proportion of the ore, generally 1/6th, obtained below these marks when drained by the sough, and a smaller proportion of any ore mined below the actual level of the sough itself. The arrangements for the installation of pumping machinery to enable the miners to work below sough level varied, as did the procedure for the maintenance of shafts and levels and even the sough.

Some soughs were not driven in this way, but were made by the miners themselves and were driven along the 'sole', or bottom level of the vein. Good examples of this this can be seen at Smallpenny Sough (181.657) in the upper reaches of Lathkill Dale; Wardlow Sough (175.747) in Cressbrook Dale, and a sough draining the western end of the Coast Rake into Gratton Dale (209.609).

The second half of the 18th century was distinguished by large ore strikes and some mines returning immense profits, although the smaller mines exploited by the working shareholders continued to be very much in evidence. The Hubberdale Mine near Flagg, was the scene of a remarkable discovery of a rich pipe in 1767, from which 14,600 loads of lead ore were extracted, at a profit of over £1 per load between that year and 1769. This sudden ore bonanza is a typical feature of pipe workings. The ore, often in large, pure lumps embedded in clay in a wide 'cavern' is suddenly lost and thins to a 'stringer' of calcite or other gangue minerals, of a ¼ inch or less. The miners follow these leadings, hoping to find a similar "Belly" or widening of the pipe. A large pipe had been worked in the 1730's at the Ball-Eye Mine in Via Gellia, where it is said £50,000 worth of lead had been extracted in a period of three years.

23

Breachside Sough near Hassop, Odin Mine at Castleton, Placket Mine at Winster, Waterhole Mine near Rowland and some of the mines on the Hucklow Edge vein were all highly productive. Blythe Sough near Alport produced nearly £33,000 worth of ore between 1790 and 1800, and similarly Shining Sough, another venture associated with the draining of the Alport mines which had been started in 1756, ten years previously to Hill Carr Sough, raised £42,000 worth of ore.

UNDERGROUND TRANSPORT AND HAULAGE :

Transport underground was to a large degree still very primitive. Old levels which have been re-opened for the first time since mining ceased have sometimes been found to contain channels made by sledges on the floor of the passages before rails were introduced underground. Many of the small mines did not have 'gates' or passages large enough to accommodate rails and tubs pulled by ponies. Only in the larger concerns do references to 'cartgates' occur. Odin Mine possesses a beautiful example of a stone lined and arched cartgate, but unfortunately this is now accessible for a short distance only.

A unique form of transport was utilised at the Speedwell Mine, Castleton. Here the undergound movement of the waste rock and the lead ore was accomplished by means of boats. This in itself was not a new idea, having been used some years before by the famous canal engineer James Brindley, who was born at Wormhill in the heart of the Peak District, at the Duke of Bridgewater's collieries at Worsley near Manchester. Boats had also been used during the driving of the Hill Carr Sough, but only to remove the waste rock. At the Speedwell Mine the intention was to transport the lead ore underground by barge haulage in a system of 'canals' or levels flooded to a convenient height, the water being diverted from a natural cave system. A most interesting fact is that the mine Agent was John Gilbert, who had been connected with Brindley's underground canal at Worsley. The principal undertaker of the scheme was Ralph Oakden of Staffordshire, who according to local tradition was ruined by the venture. Although he may have made an overall loss at Speedwell Mine, it is now known that he, or a relation of the same name, perhaps a son, was involved in mining elsewhere in the Castleton and Bradwell areas. The main level, referred to in an old reckoning book as Oakden Level, and elsewhere as Navigation Mine, was driven between 1774 and 1781. Although other soughs besides the Hill Carr utilised boat haulage to remove waste rock, and the Magpie Sough transported lead ore in a boat to the level mouth, Speedwell Mine remains unique as a mine specifically planned to utilise boat haulage underground.

The raising of the ore to the surface was either up a number of small, shallow shafts by hand winches known as 'stowes' or 'stoces', or by horse gin up the usually deeper and wider 'engine shafts'. A typical surface feature of lead mining ground is the still conspicuous 'gin circle'. The winding drum was horizontal, and was operated by a horse walking in a circle, the winding ropes passing over pulleys and so into the shaft. The ore and rock was wound in a large bucket known as a 'kibble'. The Gregory Mine near Ashover had a steam 'whimsey' or winding engine erected by 1796 but it was not until the 19th century that the more important mines had steam winding engines. Before this, men entered the mine by either a level or a series of short climbing shafts. The climbing shafts were generally about 50 feet deep, with a short level at the bottom, at the end of which would be another short shaft, so leading in stages to the deepest parts of the mine. These shafts had pieces of wood called "stemples" let into the walls at both sides of the shaft, and the miners descended and ascended on these crude ladders. More rarely stone footholds were used,

Descending a shaft by means of a stow in a coe (from L. Simonin).

and a good example of this latter arrangement can be seen at the rear of the Cottage at the Magpie Mine, near Sheldon.

Parallel with the diverse use of pumping apparatus, the varied methods of underground haulage, and the raising of materials to the surface, all existed and functioned side by side. An old Monyash miner, Mr. Charles H. Millington, who died in 1968, aged 90, vividly remembered hand-drilling shot holes by the light of tallow candles in mines near Monyash. These mines, though not deep, were entered by means of climbing shafts, the mineral being wound up by hand stowes.

25

THE YEARS 1800 - 1850. THE ERA OF THE LARGER MINING COMPANIES :
The opening of the 19th century witnessed a further development in the working and more particularly the management of Derbyshire lead mining. The London Lead Company, the larger Sough partnerships, the Smelting concerns and certain individuals such as the Bagshaws, had brought capital investment to a mineral field in which the small mine worked by miner/shareholders was a predominant feature.

The driving of Hill Carr Sough in the latter half of the 18th century gave a new lease of life to the mines south of the River Lathkill, near Alport, but the veins rapidly became exhausted down to the level of the sough by the beginning of the 19th century and better drainage became a necessity. In 1801 the proprietors of Hill Carr Sough and the proprietors of the Shining Sough invited the noted Cornish engineer Richard Trevithick to submit plans for the deeper drainage of the mines. He came to Derbyshire from Cornwall to examine the mines and ultimately proposed the erection of a water pressure engine. These engines utilised the pressure exerted by a falling column of water acting on a piston working the pump rods. Trevithick's engine started work in 1805 and was probably located at the Crash Purse Shaft. Later it was moved to another shaft. A column of water in 15 inches diameter pipes descended 150 feet, working the piston, the cylinder being situated at sough level. The engine was capable of lifting 280 gallons of water per minute from 8 fathoms below Hill Carr Sough, consuming 416 gallons in the process. Both the pumped water and the water used to drive the engine flowed away down the sough.

During 1839 the mines were consolidated into one company calling itself the Alport Mining Company. They erected other hydraulic engines, amongst them the famous Guy Engine, a model of which is in the Science Museum, London. The downfall column of water for this engine was 132 feet contained in 40 inches diameter iron pipes, the engine being placed 210 feet below the surface. The water to work it was brought from the River Lathkill, over the village of Alport by an aqueduct, into a drift which conveyed it to the Guy shaft. The Alport mines were ultimately worked 21 fathoms below the level of Hill Carr Sough but the immense quantities of water, believed by John Taylor, a man of wide mining experience, to be the largest on record in the history of mining, forced the Company to wind up in 1852. Undoubtedly the crippling pumping costs were the prime factor in the premature closing of this mining venture, as many thousands of loads of ore had been obtained, and it was known that rich and promising veins were left untouched. The falling prices of lead did not help to keep the Company sufficiently interested to exploit undeveloped areas. Later, smaller companies worked parts of the ground with resultant profits.

A little higher up the Lathkill valley, the Mandale Mine had been worked on a large scale from 1797 when a sough was driven up the vein. Large quantities of ore were found in 1820 and again in 1823, although the undertaking as a whole resulted in an overall loss. In 1839 the Lathkill Dale Mine, which had been restarted in 1825 after 50 years of virtual idleness, amalgamated with the Mandale Mine.

Between 1834 and 1836 the Lathkill Company had erected a huge 52 feet diameter water wheel, capable of pumping no less than 4,000 gallons of water per minute from a depth of twenty fathoms. This wheel was made at the Duckmanton Foundry of Benjamin Smith and Co. and cost over £500. In 1840 another smaller wheel, 35 feet in diameter was erected a little lower down the valley at the Mandale Mine, pumping from 90 feet below the level of the River Lathkill. Later in 1847 a Cornish engine made by Messrs. Grahams, Milton Ironworks, Elsecar, was also erected at this latter mine. The cylinder was 65 inches in diameter and the engine was rated at 165 horse-power. The water influx was, like Lathkill Dale mine, a very acute problem, and the mine was abandoned in 1851.

Sheffield businessmen invested large sums of money in some of the Derbyshire mines and a good example is the Moorwood Sough Company, later the Eyam Mining Company. The Moorwood Sough (237.744) was originally started in the 18th century, being projected to unwater the Eyam Edge mines, but it was abandoned, This led to the formation in 1843 of the Moorwood Sough Co. with the intention of continuing the sough to the mines in Eyam village and those on the Edge. A year later, William Wyatt, a well known 'lead mine Agent and shareholder in mines.all over Derbyshire, proposed that a branch sough be started with the eventual aim of draining the Watergrove Mine. This branch sough was abandoned in the 1860's, south of the main road in Middleton Dale. In 1849 the Eyam Mining Company took over the rights of the Moorwood Sough Co. and extended many of the mines in and around Eyam. They deepened to 1,092 feet the New Engine Mine (224.763) on Eyam Edge and in 1863 erected a steam pumping engine made by Davy Bros. of Sheffield. The shaft is reputedly the deepest in Derbyshire and the chimney, once a well-known feature, was demolished in August, 1973.

Alderman Fairburn, also of Sheffield, re-opened Calver Sough Mine (239.747). A large Cornish engine, made at the Bowling Ironworks, Bradford, in 1848 worked at the mine until 1863. This engine had a cylinder of 70 inches diameter.

By 1863 the mine was abandoned and the engine was removed 5 years later to Magpie Mine, Sheldon. Later it was again moved, this time to the Manvers Colliery, near Ilkeston, but its ultimate fate is unknown.

An ambitions project was started at the High Rake Mine (164.778) near Great Hucklow in 1832. The old miners had been content to work this portion of the Hucklow Edge Vein in the top beds of limestone overlying the toadstone. An abortive attempt had been made in 1757 to sink through this bed into the limestone underneath, and again in 1768. This idea was not tried again until 1832, at which date the High Rake Mining Company was formed with the object of sinking through the toadstone into the underlying limestone. By 1852 this shaft had been sunk a total depth of 120 fathoms but was still in toadstone, and on the basis of reports of P. C. Gillott, a Chesterfield mining engineer, the mine was abandoned after losing over £19,000. The steam engine was made by Graham & Co., Milton Ironworks, Elsecar, near Barnsley, and was made on the Simms principle, having two cylinders. The high pressure steam acted in a cylinder of 36 inches diameter, and was then exhausted into a larger one of 70 inches diameter. The mine also had a steam whimsey or winding engine bought from the Magpie Mine. The engine was later sold to the Mixon Mining Co. having been valued at £1,147. This latter Company mined copper in Staffordshire.

The heyday of Derbyshire lead mining was now coming to an end. The Odin Mine which had worked continuously for very nearly two hundred years, mostly with large profits, closed in 1869, even though a low level sough had been driven from Trickett Bridge (SK 150.833) in Castleton. Commenced in 1816, it reached Odin Vein in 1822, and was continued up the vein well into the 1840's, reaching Peak Forest Liberty by 1850. One of the chief proprietors of the mine in these last years was Robert How Ashton, of Losehill Hall, who was a well known lead-mine owner and who additionally owned the lead smelting works at Brough.

The Peak Forest Mining Company commenced operations in 1858 to re-work the Coalpithole Mine. This venture was financed largely by Sheffield businessmen,

27

but closed in the 1880's. The Company spent a good deal of money sinking new shafts and erecting pumping and winding machinery. The pumping shaft (098.813) over 400 feet deep, was at the side of the road at Perryfoot; and another very deep shaft, reputedly 110 fathoms in depth, was sunk through a considerable thickness of shale at the western extremity of the vein. The mine was one of the few to have a steam winding engine, made by Bray & Co., Leeds, in 1853 for Brightside Mine, Hassop. It was a horizontal engine used for pumping as well as winding. In 1870 it was sold to the Peak Forest Mining Co. for £188.

THE DECLINING YEARS : 1850 TO THE PRESENT DAY :

After 1860 there was a rapid decline in the numbers of men employed in lead mining in the county. In 1861, 2,333 men were engaged in the industry, this number falling in 1881 to 871, and to a mere 285 in 1901.

One exception to this general run-down stands out, and that is the case of the Mill Close Mine, Darley Dale. This mine, after standing idle for many years, was re-opened in 1859 by E. M. Wass, who also owned the Lea Lead Works. At the time of his death in 1886, the mine had produced over 36,000 tons of lead ore. Afterwards the production figures remained high, and ultimately three pumping engines were employed, raising over 7,000,000 gallons of water per day. At the same time, in excess of 800 tons of crude lead ore were brought to the surface to be dressed and smelted, and zinc ore was obtained in fairly large quantities. The mine finally closed just before the Second World War due to the failure to locate new ore bearing ground, the low price of lead on the market and the immense pumping costs. These factors, coupled with the prospect of having to sink a new shaft, possibly 1,000 feet deep, for haulage and ventilation purposes, made the continuance of this great mine an impossibility.

During this century there have been several speculative attempts to re-open old mines, and some have produced some ore for limited periods, but none have been able to sustain a high level of production for a long enough period. Acting on the advice of an old Middleton miner, the Blobber Mine (281.533) near Wirksworth located good ore in the early 1920's but this soon ran out. Today, fluorspar, the mineral discarded by the old miners as worthless, is a far more valuable commodity than lead. Large mines at Eyam and Longstone Edge are producing considerable quantities of this mineral which, along with the output from surface dumps and smaller mines, makes the Peak District one of the world's leading producers. Some thousands of tons of lead-ore form a valuable by-product so that it may be said that lead-mining is still an active industry.

Calcite, barytes and limestone are mined on a more limited scale. Two mines on the Long Rake near Youlgreave work calcite, and limestone is mined at Middleton-by-Wirksworth.

So the old mines are virtually neglected. The miners of bygone days would no doubt be amazed at the modern techniques employed in today's mining industry.

A mineral-lined cavity or vug in a pipe vein. Magpie Mine Sough.

A miner's dish used for measuring lead ore. The inscription is GR 1770

The horse-winding gin on Snake Mine, Hopton Wood, about 1913. The shaft, 250 feet deep, is under the pulley, and the barrel alongside was used to raise ore.

(By courtesy of Derbyshire Pennine Club)

Calcite Dog Tooth crystals on lead ore.

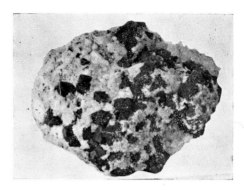

Octahedral galena crystals with white calcite.

Banded encrusted barytes (white) and galena.

Cubes of clear fluorspar.

Cockscomb crystals of barytes.

Nodules of barytes on dark limestone.

Typical specimens of Peak District Minerals.   (*Dr. T. D. Ford*).

A typical Peak District mineral vein – Blue John fluorspar and calcite between walls of limestone, Treak Cliff Cavern.   (*Dr. T. D. Ford*).

"Nicking" Greaves Croft Mine, Moss Rake, Bradwell, 1906. (*Photograph by the late F. J. Brindley*).

The last Peak District lead-miner – the late C. H. Millington, at Monyash. (*H. M. Parker*).

Watt's Engine House, Mill Close Mine.   (*F. Nixon*).

The Engine House, head-frame and chimney of Mill Dam Mine, Great Hucklow, about 1900. The building in the left background became the Theatre.

Top left:
A small hand-picked level in Hillocks Mine.
(*J. Matthews*).

Top right:
Looking up a hand-picked shaft in Hillocks Mine.
The ladder rungs provide a scale as they are 7 inches
long. (*J. Robey*).

Bottom left:
Details of pick marks in Knotlow Mine. (*J. Robey*).

Bottom right:
A typical Peak District Sough; Shining Sough in the
Alport Mines. (*A. E. Marsh*).

The top of Mandale Forefield Shaft showing the Ginging. (*H. M. Parker*).

An explorer descending Field Grove Engine Shaft, Sheldon, by wire-ladder. The section cut off by timbers was originally the ladder-way. (*H. M. Parker*).

Model of a crushing circle (model by H. E. Chatburn). (*H. M. Parker*).

Model of a horse-gin (model by H. E. Chatburn). (*H. M. Parker*).

The arched tail of Red Rake Sough, 1951. (*H. M. Parker*).

Looking out of the stone-arched Red Rake Sough Tail. (*H. M. Parker*).

The Odin crushing circle and wheel, near Castleton. (*M. E. Smith*).

A water-colour by John Webber of Odin Mine and Mam Tor, Castleton, in 1789. The waste-hillocks have now largely been used in road-making. (*Reproduced by permission of the Whitworth Art Gallery*).

The buildings of Magpie Mine, Sheldon.   (*H. M. Parker*).

Three generations of winding house at Magpie Mine: the Cornish Engine House of c. 1869 in the background; the 1913 winding drum in the foreground; and the 1950 corrugated shed. The shaft is beneath the head-frame in the centre.   (*H. M. Parker*).

Mining fluorspar in Ladywash Mine today   (*By courtesy of Laporte Industries Ltd., Glebe Mine, Eyam*).

The oldest industrial chimney in Britain: at Stone Edge cupola, built about 1770. (*H. M. Parker*).

ITINERARIES

1. The Castleton Area

Lying at the northern extremity of the limestone massif, Castleton has numerous mineral veins outcropping, and has had a long history of mining. Lead has been worked since Roman times, if not earlier; Blue John Fluorspar has been mined at least since the 18th century, and in the last few decades there has been intermittent working, mostly at outcrop, for barytes, calcite and fluorspar. Two separate walks are advised to cover all the important features still to be seen, though of course it is possible to modify the route and combine the walks if desired.

(a) The Veins and Mines south and west of Castleton. 2½ inches: 1 mile Map SK 18. 6 inches: 1 mile SK 18 SW & SE. Walking distance 4-5 miles.

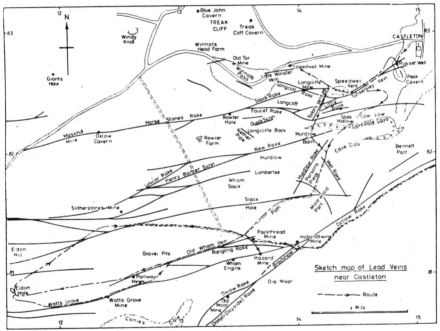

Map of the lead veins near Castleton.

From Castleton village car park follow the Peakshole stream to Peak Cavern gorge. On the east side of the entrance to the gorge is **Russet Well** (148.827). This is an important spring draining the mines and veins lying to the WEST of the gorge, so that the water must pass under the gorge and Peakshole Water before rising. In times of flood, water backs up in this hidden area and overflows via Peakshole Sough and Peak Cavern.

45

Peakshole Sough is recorded as being driven westwards beneath Cowlow between about 1770 and 1786. The Sough tail may be seen in the garden of the Peak Cavern custodian's house. The walls of Peak Cavern Gorge here show traces of shallow surface working in thin veins known as scrins. **Peak Cavern** (149.826) is open to tourists and should be visited as a prime example of what the old miners called a "self-open"—a natural cavern suitable for disposal of unwanted water or waste, though in this case there is little evidence of mining activities within the cavern. The visitor's route extends ½ mile, and explorers have penetrated over a mile further largely beneath the upper reaches of Cavedale. In the cavern a thin vein, largely calcite, may be seen crossing Roger Rain's House, where surface water leaking in from Cavedale is responsible for the "rain".

Leaving Peak Cavern, turn left up the lane behind Goosehill Hall and take the footpath along the foot of **Cowlow**. The path partly follows the line of Tankersley Vein, but little can be seen today. The path bends to the right and just before a gate (143.825) there is an outcrop of Toadstone, the volcanic agglomerate of the Speedwell Vent believed to have once been the throat of a small volcano. Above and to the left a steep gully known as Cowlow Nick (142.824) separates Cowlow from Long Cliff and several scrin veins may be seen crossing it. A bank about 100 yards from the path has the remains of a miners' coe on it (142.825). Halfway up the face of Long Cliff, there is a line of prominent mounds marking shafts on the Longcliff Rake. From the highest of those, Slack Rake branches up the hill, and the intersection is marked by the mound and partly run-in shaft of **Longcliff Mine** (140.825), which is sunk partly in a natural pothole and is over 100 feet deep.

Walk to the foot of the Winnats Pass, where a visit may be made to the **Speedwell Mine** (139.827) operated as a tourist cavern. From a depth of 70 feet below the Winnats road, a mine level was driven due south beneath Longcliff between about 1774 and 1781, to intersect the above-mentioned veins of Longcliff at depth. They were unfortunately relatively poor in lead-ore and the miners' main objective, Faucet Rake, was found to have been washed out to form a large natural cavern now known as the Bottomless Pit. Further on a series of stream caves were struck near New Rake, and the water was diverted into the level to make a canal tunnel, with boats for haulage of ore and waste rock, following the pattern successfully established by James Brindley in the Duke of Bridgewater's coal mines near Manchester. Tourists may still travel through the first part of the tunnel as far as the Bottomless Pit by boat, and they can easily appreciate the magnitude of the task which faced the 18th century miner tunnelling ½ mile through solid limestone.

Leaving the Speedwell Mine, the road should be taken back to the village, and then the footpath up Cavedale from the market place. A short-cut may be taken across Cowlow, though there is no footpath, either by the gently rising track up the hillside, or by the more energetic scramble up the scree of old mining operations in Cowlow Nick up the line of Tailors Venture Vein. At the top of the gully, Hurdlow Barn (141.821) lies at the eastern end of the now much overgrown hillocks of New Rake. Some 600 feet below the surface the Speedwell Mine canal tunnel broke into the stream caves beneath Hurdlow Barn. Near the upper part of **Cavedale** are the lines or workings on Hurdlow Rake and Wet Rake, the latter with blocks of quartz-rock scattered in the hollows. The footpath in Cavedale leads southwestwards, partly along the line of workings in Slack Hole Rake, and up to the Old Moor Road near **Hazard Mine** (136.812). Here there are extensive hillocks, largely of calcite, from the mid 19th century workings. Near the engine shaft, now covered with an iron grill, is the remains of a jigging apparatus used during the early part of this century to recover lead from the hillocks, which are now being reworked yet again for fluorspar and barytes. The remains of a gin-circle, partly shielded by a wall, may also be seen. Hazard Mine was worked to a depth of 600 feet, though the engine shaft is only about 350 feet deep. It was connected at times with **Hollandtwine Mine** (140.813), some 300 yards to the northeast, and the drainage of both was turned into a "Great Swallow" in the latter at over 600 feet depth. Nothing is known of this natural drainage, but it is thought that the water flowed into Peak Cavern. The hillocks of Hollandtwine Mine still carry crushing and gin-circles, and the main shaft is open to a depth of 350 feet, but at Hazard Mine the recent removal of the hillocks has destroyed many of the old coes.

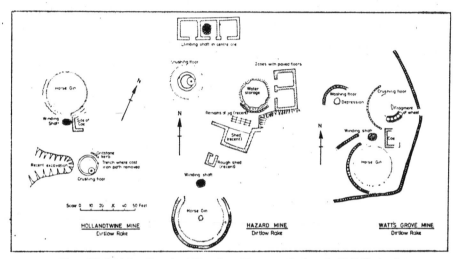

Plans of Hollandtwine, Hazard and Watts Grove Mines, near Castleton (by H. E. Chatburn).

West of Hollandtwine Mine, **Dirtlow Rake** splits into several branches. Hazard Mine is on one of these and further west are **Wham Engine Mine** (134.811) and the **Portway Mines** (127.810). To the southwest runs **Oxlow Rake**, with the large hillocks of the Old Moor Mines (134.808). Many of the hillocks of these have been reworked for barytes in recent years, particularly around Portway Mines. An open-cast working in the Old Wham vein was on the site of "Gravel Pits" marked on the Ordnance Survey maps (128.811), but the remaining material shows that this was vein material in loose lumps resulting from the weathering away of the surrounding limestone, and that the "gravel" was in fact lumps of barytes with some galena. Blocks of quartz rock, with adherent goethite pseudo-morphing marcasite may also be found here, as well as blocks with what appear to be worm-holes which are in fact casts of fossil corals.

If time permits it is worth walking a further half mile due west across the fields to **Eldon Hole** (116.809), on the south flank of Eldon Hill. This open natural pothole is over 100 feet long and about 200 feet deep, and there are legends of a goose being thrown down to emerge several days later from Peak Cavern, with "its feathers singed by the fires of hell". Though this latter is unlikely, the natural drainage of the

47

Coalpithole Mine, a mile further west, must pass under Eldon Hill en route towards Castleton. The return from Eldon Hole may be made either by going northeasterly over the hill to rejoin the Old Moor Road near the maze of veins by **Slitherstones Mine** (125.815), or by following the Watts Grove Vein along the south flank of Eldon Hill. Overlooking Conies Dale is **Watts Grove Mine** (124.808), with the gin circle and crushing floor still clearly visible. The open engine shaft is about 200 feet deep.

From Hazard and Hollandtwine Mines the Old Moor Road skirts along the south side of Dirtlow Rake, and the opportunity should be taken at intervals to look into the open-cut. A gradual change in the character of the gangue minerals, and hence the hillocks takes place. Around Hazard Mine the gangue is mostly opaque white calcite, but near Hollandtwine Mine pink and yellow barytes become more common. Above the north wall of **Pindale** just south of the hairpin bend in the road (159.824), pale blue fluorite can form as much as half the vein filling, interbanded with cream-coloured barytes. But this change is patchy and opposite the junction with the road to Tideswell (153.820) the rake can be seen to be mostly calcite in radiating clusters of white crystals. Galena is developed mostly against the walls of the vein, and the grooves on the walls of the present open-cut show how the "old man" followed these strings of lead-ore down the cheeks of the vein by means of picked-out shafts. The south wall of the open-cut here shows a strong development of quartz rock, and numerous blocks may be seen in the adjacent field to the south.

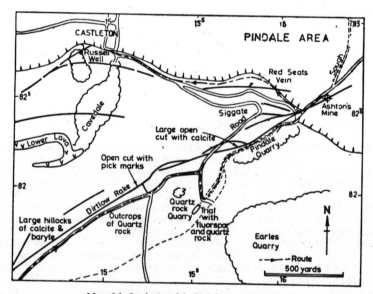

Map of the Lead veins of the Pindale Area, Castleton.

Dirtlow Rake has been worked opencast down the north side of Pindale, and beyond the foot of the dale **Ashton's Mine** (163.826) was sunk through the shales to reach the buried part of the rake. Little is known of the underground extent of the

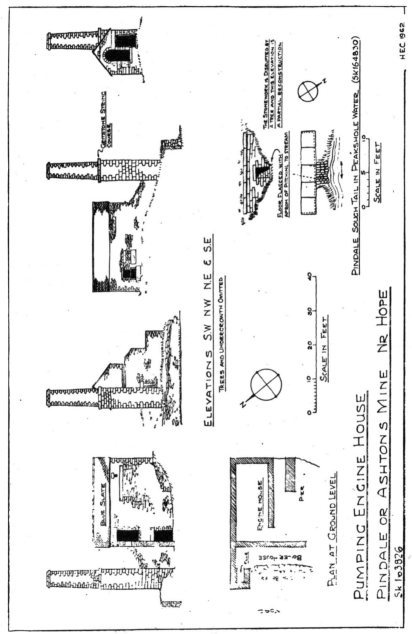

ELEVATIONS S.W. N.W. N.E. & S.E.
TREES AND UNDERGROWTH OMITTED

CRITSTONE STRING COURSE

BLUE SLATE

ENGINE HOUSE

PIER

BOILER HOUSE

PLAN AT GROUND LEVEL

SCALE IN FEET
0 10 20 30 40

THE STONEWORK IS DISRUPTED BY A TREE AND THIS ELEVATION IS A PARTIAL RECONSTRUCTION

FLOOR FLAGGED WITH APRON OF PITCHING TO STREAM

PINDALE SOUTH TAIL IN PEAKSHOLE WATER. (SK164830)

SCALE IN FEET
0 5 10

PUMPING ENGINE HOUSE
PINDALE OR ASHTONS MINE NR HOPE

SK 163826

HEC 1962

Ashton's (Pindale) Mine, Dirtlow Rake, Castleton (by H. E. Chatburn).

workings, as the Pindale Sough which drained this mine towards the river with its tail close by the footpath ¼ mile to the north at 164.831 is blocked and flooded, but the shaft is said to have been sunk largely in toadstone beneath the shale, with no regular vein. The engine house and chimney still stand on the hillock in more or less their original form. An agreement to drive the sough survives, with the date 1743, and it may be presumed that the sough was driven during the following decade. In 1800-1802 it was producing more lead than the rich Odin Mine. At this point one can contrast the small scale and shortage of capital of the leadmining operations with the vast scale of Earle's cement works and its limestone quarry and shale pits.

The hill spur to the north of Pindale has numerous scrins in which a number of minerals may be found. Red Seats Vein runs westwards along the foot of the hill below the Pindale-Castleton road, and is one of the few veins in the district yielding a considerable proportion of zinc minerals. Sphalerite (ZnS), better known locally as blende or blackjack, can be found, but calamine ($ZnCO_3$) is more common. Often known to the miners as "dry-bone" this is an inconspicuous cream-coloured porous mineral once used in the manufacture of brass.

The return to Castleton may be made following the footpath below Red Seats Vein westwards.

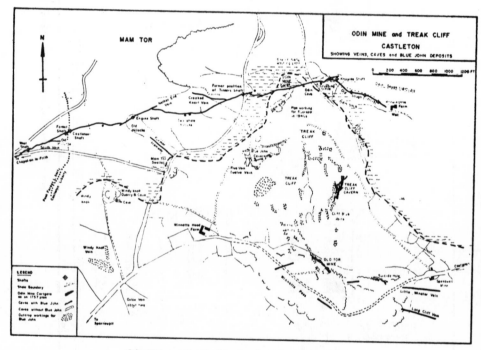

Odin Mine and the Blue John deposits of Treak Cliff, Castleton.

(b)   Odin Mine and the Blue John veins of Treak Cliff: Walking distance about 2¼ miles. 6 inches : 1 mile Ordnance Map SK 18 SW.

From Castleton village take Hollowford Lane, northwards towards Losehill. After about 200 yards the Peakshole stream is crossed and some 20 yards further on a trickle of water emerges from a low slabbed arch in the wall on the left (west) (150.832). This is the tail (outfall) of **Odin Sough,** a drainage level proposed in 1772, but not started until 1816 and it only reached the vein in 1822, and was still being driven along the vein below the Forest shaft in 1850. From Trickett Bridge the west-northwesterly course is marked by shafts and tips of shale at about 1,000 ft. intervals and it reached the vein at a depth of 240 feet below Knowles Shaft. The sough then followed the vein beneath the south flank of Mam Tor as far as the Peak Forest Liberty boundary, where it must have been some 800 feet below surface. Return into Castleton and take the main road westwards for ¼ mile. Look for a stile on the right between the houses opposite the entrance to Peak Cavern car park (locally known as Jewel or Duel Yard). The stile leads to a public footpath alongside the Odin Sitch, which has banks exposing shales in places. After ¾ mile at the crossing of the lane to Dunscar Farm (143.833) one of the shale hillocks on Odin Sough can be seen to the right. Do not cross the Sitch but continue straight on to Knowlegates Farm, where a spring in the stream bank marks the tail of an earlier Odin Sough driven in the 1660s some 126 feet higher than the 19th century sough.

Using the stile behind the farm climb the rough ground of the Mam Tor landslips on the the hillocks of **Odin Mine,** where Knowles Shaft is still open, though flooded (135.835). It was originally 240 feet deep to the sough, though it has probably collapsed below the present flood level. The adjacent hillocks provide a variety of mineral specimens, but they did not all come from Odin Mine as ores were brought here for crushing and washing from some miles away. The crushing wheel with its iron tyre and circular iron track were erected about 1823 at a cost of about £40. Still preserved, the crusher consists of a Gritstone wheel about 5 ft. 10 ins. diameter and 12 ins. wide; a square hole 11½ inches wide passes through the centre. The wheel is shod with an iron tyre, 2 inches thick which was held in place by wooden wedges; the remains of a wooden shaft pass through the centre hole. The crusher ran on a circular iron track 15 inches wide and about 18 ft. diameter. The track is built up of 8 segments, 2 inches thick, and is bolted together on the under side with fish plates; the whole of the track is bedded on fine gravel. The centre pivot block is missing. Close to the crusher was the entrance of the Cartgate, the main haulage level into Odin Mine. This ran beneath the road and followed the vein beneath Odin Gorge, but nothing can be seen now owing to the debris of road-widening.

Odin Mine is reputed to have been worked in Saxon, if not Roman, times, but the first recorded evidence of a mine named Odin is about 1280, which makes it the oldest record of a named mine in Derbyshire. By 1663 the workings had apparently extended far enough for there to be a dispute about drainage agreements. It was worked almost continuously throughout the 18th century, with annual production of 100 to 800 tons of lead ore. Peak periods were in the 1720s, 1770s, and about 1800. The sough was proposed in 1772 but does not appear to have been completed until about 1845 to judge from the ore accounts.

Across the road the open gash of Odin Gorge lies at the northern margin of the limestone outcrop (134.834). The Gorge is in fact artificial, as it is where the vein has been completely removed. Its wall shows traces of minerals, including blue fluorspar and galena, as well as horizontal slickensides (grooving on the limestone walls owing to fault movements grinding one wall against the other). A small branch

51

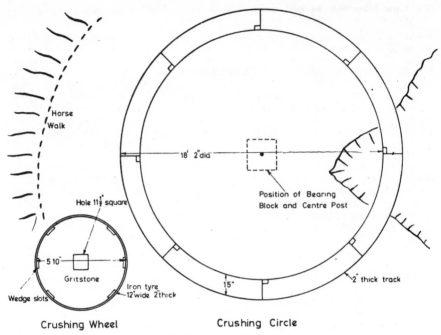

Crushing Wheel   Crushing Circle

The Odin Mine crushing circle and wheel.

vein at the entrance to the gorge shows deposits of the unusual white clay allophane. With the use of ropes and ladders it is possible for expert mine explorers to descend into the workings at the back of the gorge, and to go in about 500 feet, but the workings are much too dangerous for the novice owing to unstable stacked waste rock. The workings are known to have extended at least a mile to the west in the mid 18th century, and working carried on at least until 1869 with some desultory attempts at re-opening in the 20th century. A number of small veins and workings in branches from Odin vein may be seen on the hillside above Odin Gorge. The present course of the stream curving in its shale floored channel round the top of Odin Gorge is artificial. At some date unknown probably in the 17th century the stream was diverted from its original course down the limestone Odin gully (above and to the south of the Gorge) as it previously flowed directly into the workings. The trace of the main rake workings may be followed by the hillocks on the south flank of Mam Tor for nearly a mile to the west-south-west. Tinkers Shaft was approximately beneath the road outside the Blue John Cavern, but nothing is visible now. A complex of branch veins was worked beneath the southern edge of the Mam Tor landslip scar but there is nothing visible on the surface. Engine Shaft (127.833) and Castleton and Forest Shafts (124.833) are marked by hollows in the hillocks, and West Forefield Shaft is in the angle made by the Chapel-Castleton and Chapel-Edale roads (123.832). The Forest shaft was at the back of the present picnic site, separated from the Castleton shaft by the Mining Liberty boundary, now marked by a fence. Beyond the West Forefield Shaft, the miners found that the shale dipped steeply down beneath the line of their workings in the limestone. About ¼ mile further west a line of hillocks (117.830) near Peakshill Farm marks the line of yet another sough driven in 1726-1729, though whether it reached the vein beneath the thick shales is debatable, as it is far beyond the known limits of workings.

From these hillocks on Odin Rake cross to the small limestone quarry in **Windy Knoll** (136.830) to see the cave which yielded numerous bones of Ice Age mammals in the 1870s, and the bitumen deposits. Collectively known as elaterite, these in fact comprise some 30 different hydrocarbons (natural oils) believed to have been distilled from the organic traces in the limestone by the hot mineralizing solutions which were responsible for forming the nearby mineral veins. Some of the hydro-,carbons cause crystal lattice deformations which give the colour to Blue John.

From Windy Knoll return to **Treak Cliff Cavern** (136.832). This tourist cavern shows the nature of the **Blue John** fluorspar veins to advantage. The entrance is via a mid 18th century adit driven into a series of caverns containing a pipe vein. Unlike the rakes and scrins with their near-vertical walls, the pipes are irregularly elongate mineral deposits following the inclination (dip) of the limestone beds. In this case the pipe is followed up the steeply dipping beds of Treak Cliff, and a series of patches of fluorspar with blue and white banding in various intensities forms the Blue John veins. Some of the best Blue John lines the walls of voids between boulders in a conglomerate of limestone boulders, seen in parts of the cavern roof. The veins have been named according to different patterns of banding, and some fourteen varieties are generally recognised. There is an oft-repeated story that Blue John was known by the Romans and was used to make vases found in ancient Rome, but no evidence to support this story has yet come to light. On the other hand the Romans are known to have imported a mineral very like Blue John from Persia. There is in fact no recorded knowledge of the existence of Blue John until the late 17th century. It was first used for ornaments about the middle of the 18th century and rapidly reached popularity owing to its being used by Matthew Boulton as a foil for the ormulu in his ornaments, and by Robert Adam as a fireplace inlay in his great 18th century stately homes, such as Kedleston Hall, near Derby. Both these uses were at their peak about 1770, and the use of Blue John for smaller ornaments and for jewellery has continued to the present day.

In 1768 Boulton tried to obtain a monopoly of the produce of the Blue John Mines, but he succeeded only in buying 14 tons of Blue John at £5 15s. 6d. per ton. About this time the annual production was about 20 tons, but later it was limited to 3 tons, and nowadays ¼ ton per annum suffices to maintain the jewellery trade.

During the 1914-18 War and for a few years afterwards, Blue John fluorspar was worked as a fluxing material for electric furnaces, and as this work declined in 1926 blasting broke through into the richly decorated stalactite caverns which now form the main attraction of Treak Cliff Cavern.

Blue John was also worked in the now-abandoned Old Tor Mine (124.828) high on the north. side of the Winnats Pass, and by opencast means on the top of Treak Cliff. The **Blue John Caverns** (132.832), also open to the public, show Blue John veins in a large series of water-worn caverns. Both Treak Cliff and Blue John Caverns should be visited to appreciate fully the varieties of Blue John and their surroundings.

2. The Slag Mill Flue, Bradwell

Before leaving the Castleton area, it is worth considering what happened to the ores. Some were doubtless transported out of the area by pack-train over one of the numerous "Jaggers' Lanes" before smelting, but most was smelted at one or other of numerous smelting sites, of which many remains can be found. The earliest sites, 'boles', were situated on high edges and hills, as they relied on the wind—as for example on Smelting Hill, east of Bradwell. Later water power was used for the blast and most of the streams locally had one or more mills on them until the late eighteenth century. No less than six works served the area in the nineteenth century; of these three have substantial remains. Most were 'cupolas', using a chimney to provide draught for a coal-fired reverberatory furnace (See Stonedge Cupola), but the Slag Mill site used water and later steam to power a blast furnace (or slag mill) to resmelt slag thrown over the cliff from an earlier site known as 'Old Cupola'. The mill was situated to the east of the Bradwell-Tideswell road, a few yards south of the village, to the left on entering the narrow part of the dale (174.808). The flues are stone-walled; they run parallel to the road southwards for several hundred feet before turning back along a parallel course to the main mill area again. The flue is soil and grass-covered for most of its length. The continuation of the flue may be seen as an open trench where the roof has disappeared; and eventually the flue disappears underground as a tunnel 6 ft. high and 3-4 feet wide. This contains branching galleries which are blocked in the region of a former chimney. The underground section of the flue is 360 ft. long and is stone arched over nearly the whole of its length. The position on the surface of the former chimney is now marked by a rubbish-filled hole. Air for the mill was piped from a water wheel at the Yeld; the square mounting frame for the water wheel and the lower end of the iron air pipe may still be seen (174.809). *

As well as a slag hearth (or mill) the works also had a calcining furnace, which was used to prepare lead ore so that it also could be smelted in the slag hearth. Originally the works were to operate for 18 months, and the lease to James Mitchell dated 1851 specifically made him liable for any poisoning to animals; to reduce this the flues were built. The works were taken over by Thomas Burgoyne of Edensor by 1854, after four men had died as a result of sulphurous fumes accumulating when the pump engine was faulty; in 1859 the works were taken over by John Fairburn, until he moved his operations to Middleton Dale in 1862. The area of land between the Mill and the Yeld was used for depositing slag. John Fairburn owned 1/20th of the shares of the Coalpithole Mine at Perryfoot and it is believed that a large part of the output of this mine (which was reopened in 1858) was taken to the Slag Mill. There are grounds for considering that the efficiency of this Mill at that time was 95%. The final date of closing of the Mill is not known but most of the surface features including the large chimney disappeared before 1912.

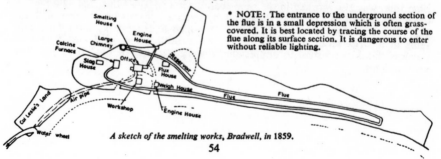

* NOTE: The entrance to the underground section of the flue is in a small depression which is often grass-covered. It is best located by tracing the course of the flue along its surface section. It is dangerous to enter without reliable lighting.

A sketch of the smelting works, Bradwell, in 1859.

3. The Eyam - Stoney Middleton Area

2¼ inches : 1 mile, Maps SK 26 and SK 27; 6 inches : 1 mile, Maps SK 26 NE & SE, SK 27 NW & SW.

The other itineraries in this book are concerned with the long and ancient history of the lead-mining industry, and the Eyam-Stoney Middleton area is inseparable from this, but history is still being made around Eyam by the modern fluorspar miners. Many of the old relics have vanished in the last few years, but new monuments of industry have appeared in their place. A brief guide only of these is given as they change so rapidly. The fluorspar mines are operated by Laporte Industries Ltd., who now produce over 200,000 tons of fluorspar per annum, some 40,000 tons of barytes, and about 4,000 tons of galena. This produce comes from the company's two mines at Ladywash and Sallet Hole, from the opencast workings on Longstone Edge, and from a number of small family businesses which "tribute" ore from opencast workings and old mine hillocks scattered over North Derbyshire.

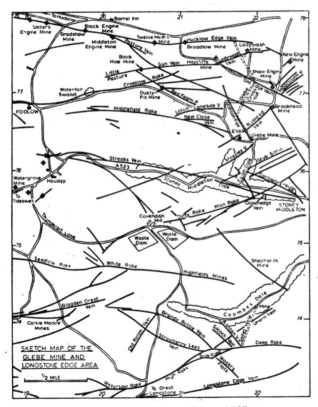

A map of the veins around Eyam and Stoney Middleton.

55

A convenient point to begin the brief tour is in the centre of Eyam, where, opposite the road up Eyam Dale and adjacent to the school the steel headgear of **Glebe Mine** stands stark against the skyline (219.764). The shaft was sunk in the 18th century to work Ashton's Pipe. After a long period of idleness it was re-fitted in the late 1930's and a cross-cut through the limestone was made in a generally northerly direction to reach **Ladywash Mine.** This latter mine, nearly 800 feet deep, was re-lined with concrete and the Old Edge and Hucklow Edge veins are now being worked over a length of about a mile. All the ore is hauled up Ladywash Shaft, and Glebe shaft itself is used only in special circumstances. By Glebe shaft was the company's first flotation plant for separating fluorspar from other minerals but it is no longer in use. Across the road, Eyam Dale House now serves as the company's offices.

From Eyam drive south via Eyam Dale and turn left towards Stoney Middleton. After about 300 yards a group of buildings on the right, partly in use as a lorry garage, is all that remains of the Lords Cupola illustrated by Chantrey in a famous engraving dated 1817. In use from 1740 to 1885, its main period of activity was in the early 19th century. Turn round and drive west along the Tideswell road (A623) for about 1½ miles to the hamlet of Housley, around which are the remains of the **Watergrove Mine** (190.758), with several shafts covered by cairns of stones. Take a left turning, and after another left turn a lane leads to the Cavendish Mill, believed to be the most modern flotation mill in Europe, and one of the largest in the world (206.752). Bearing right past the mill, a private road leads down into Coombs Dale, to **Sallet Hole Mine** (219.741). Here an old 18th century drainage level penetrating into Longstone Edge from the north-east has been enlarged and re-equipped in the last few years, and underground mining is in progress at a depth of some 350 feet in Deep Rake. Return past the mill to the lane junction and turn left, and then fork left to reach Longstone Edge, a notable view-point with vistas over Bakewell, Longstone and Ashford. For nearly 2 miles the Deep Rake-High Rake-Watersaw Rake Vein has been worked opencast in places to a depth of 100 feet, but the opencut has been back-filled with mine waste, so as to restore the landscape. The parallel Longstone Edge vein at the foot of the Edge has also been worked opencast along much of its length. The white scars on the hillside will doubtless become grassed over in a few years' time, and little evidence will remain of this highly successful mining venture.

Return to Housley and take the road up to Bretton Edge. Note the line of old hillocks along the foot of the Edge marking the course of the Hucklow Edge Vein beneath Black Engine, Bradshaw and Slater's Engine Mines. Passing the isolated Barrel Inn (200.779), the road winds eastwards for about a mile past the private drive up to **Ladywash Mine** on the left. Ahead lies the **New Engine Mine** with its boiler and engine house still in good repair (224.774). The chimney once made a conspicuous landmark but it has recently been demolished. The shaft was sunk through hundreds of feet of sandstone and shale, and reached its final depth of 1,092 feet about 1860. It is thus the deepest lead mine shaft in Derbyshire. The engine was made by Davy Bros. of Sheffield and installed in 1863. It was last worked in 1884, since when the lower part has been flooded and the beam from the engine has somehow become wedged part way down the shaft.

On the return towards Eyam, the hillocks of **Shaw Engine Mine** are visible at the road junction ¼ mile south-west of New Engine (222.771). Below the road at the next bend are the hillocks of **Brookhead Mine** (221.768), and from them there are good views over Eyam, and the lines of old workings and hillocks stand out across the fields.

56

4. The Sheldon and Ashford Area

2¼ inches: 1 mile map SK 16; 6 inches: 1 mile—Map SK 16 NE. Walking distance 2½-4 miles.

THE MAGPIE AND NEARBY MINES

The remains of lead mining activity at Magpie Mine are as complete as anything remaining in Derbyshire. This mine, with a long and fascinating history, has much to offer both to the serious student of mining history and also to the casual observer. The mine buildings and other surface relics can all be seen within a small area and examined at leisure. The other mines described in the excursions are generally speaking smaller, but all offer varied examples of the lead mining industry, and some provide excellent geological and mineralogical specimens.

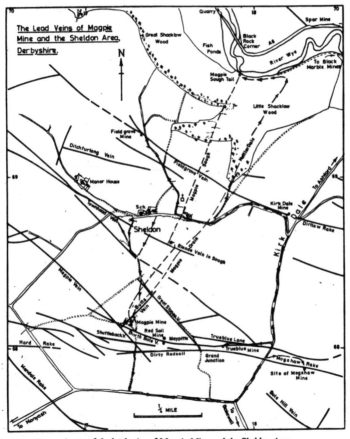

A map of the lead veins of Magpie Mine and the Sheldon Area.

57

The excursion commences in the village of Sheldon (175.688), a quiet old-world village situated on a limestone plateau, 2½ miles west of Bakewell, and 500 feet above the valley of the River Wye. The route, 3 miles long, is easy walking throughout and passes the famous Magpie Mine, Mogshaw Mine, True Blue Mine, Kirk Dale Mine and Fieldgrove Mine. Only two of these mines can be visited by car so that vehicles should be parked in Sheldon village.

Leaving Sheldon by one of the four footpaths leading in a southerly direction, the ruined engine-house and chimney stack of Magpie Mine can soon be seen upon the horizon. The best footpaths are those adjoining the school, on the opposite side of the road to the chapel, or that on the opposite side of the road to the Woodman's Cottage shop at the extreme eastern end of the village. All footpaths however converge on Magpie Mine.

The Magpie Mine: (172.682). This contains over twenty open shafts and a number of ruined buildings; it is wise therefore to stay on the well-defined paths connecting the various points of interest and to keep children and pets away from the shafts and buildings themselves. The property is now in the tenancy of the Peak District Mines Historical Society who use the main buildings as a Field Centre. Each weekend, and often during midweek periods, members of the Society will be at the Centre and pleased to help visitors.

The history of the Magpie Mine can be followed for over 230 years and a surprising number of remains from each period of working can still be seen. Local tradition says that the mine has been worked for over 300 years.

Earliest records of the mine show it being worked on a small scale, producing 40 loads of ore in 1740, probably from the area on the south side of the present cottage, close to the founder shaft on Magpie Vein. In the 1760s the mine was again worked, by George Goodwin of Monyash, who at the same period sank a horse engine shaft on Shuttlebank Vein, which was later to become the Magpie Engine Shaft, from 1802 to 1835. He was probably driven out by water at about 360 feet depth.

In 1786 the mine was 'given' by the Barmaster to Joshua White, whose shares then passed to Peter Holme and partners. They worked the mine from the founder and nearby climbing shaft until 1793 when it closed again. The main relic of this time is the rather unusual climbing shaft with projecting foot-stones, near the long boiler house, sunk 60 feet on Bole Vein in 1789.

In 1801 Peter Holme and Partners, encouraged perhaps by better prices for ore, re-opened the mine again. In order to establish a sound title, they arranged for an employee, Joseph Gregory to 'nick' and take possession of the mine after which he 'sold' it back to them for one shilling. At the same time Holme took the title to other veins in the area which were not being worked; this was the first stage in the mine's growth. Work immediately began to re-open the old Shuttlebank Engine Shaft, which was vertical down to 360 feet rather than the inconvenient series of shafts and sumps at the old Magpie. This was then linked at 50 fathoms depth to the old workings, an event duly celebrated in 'ale for the miners', and mining proper commenced, but with little success. Like Goodwin before him, Holme was driven out of the deeper workings 'on account of the water' despite the use of the horse gin and barrels to wind the water to the surface, to run down the 'Magpie Drain' towards the Wye.

The next workings continued from 1804 to late 1806, along the 50 fathom level of Magpie Gate, which was carried north-west for about a hundred yards from near the Engine Shaft. High lead prices made this nearly pay for itself—but a cross-cut to Bole Vein, only 15 feet away, led to disappointment for it was full of 'old man', the debris of earlier miners. Nevertheless working continued, and in about 1808 a further crosscut, again only a few feet, took the miners into what they called North Bole Vein, from which, by using an 'old man's sump' they appear to have found the lead finally in about 1810. It took two years more to develop the mine properly, with another and longer crosscut to form a direct route back to the winding shaft, but in 1813, in a few months, the mine recorded profits of over £360. Profits continued until in 1820 the mine paid out almost £2,000 to its shareholders, then a handsome sum for a relatively small mine.

After 1820, production went into decline and costs rose as workings got deeper, and the water almost unmanageable. In 1823 £80 was spent in two weeks on men handpumping water (at about 2 shillings per man per day) and it is clear a deep trial was being carried out to try the vein at depth. It was successful, the ground was 'laid out' by a surveyor, and sinking of the present Main Shaft (with the headstocks) began simultaneously with rising upwards from the 50 fathom level above a sump down to 80 fathoms; the two drivages met, an excellent piece of early surveying, duly celebrated in ale. By 1824 a late-Newcomen-type engine with a cylinder of 42 inches diameter and 9 feet stroke was installed by the Ashover and Chesterfield engineer Francis Thompson, and workings carried down from 70 fathoms to a total depth of about 100 fathoms in the area immediately below the shaft, with William Wyatt replacing Peter Holme as agent. 1827 saw almost 3,000 loads of lead ore, about 800 tons, produced; this was only exceeded in 1871. By the 1830s however, this bonanza was checked, again by water, and work began to explore the area laterally: the 'double' climbing and winding Crossvein Shaft, sunk in 1833, forms part of this phase. By 1835, however, the mine had closed again, for the shareholders were unwilling to contribute to any more 'calls'.

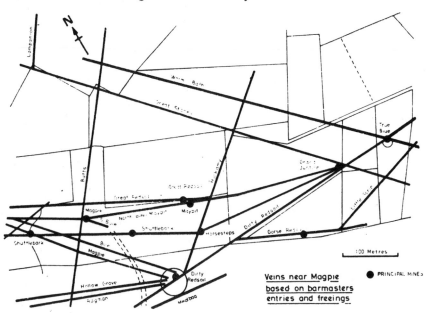

Veins near Magpie
based on barmasters
entries and freeings

100 Metres

● PRINCIPAL MINES

The years 1824 to 1835 were marred by legal disputes and 'violence on the mine', resulting in the 'murders' of 1833. What profits the mine made were absorbed by lawyers; the wily Brittlebank who successfully represented Magpie was described in one account as 'not the only knave in Derbyshire'. The quarrels began almost as soon as the new engine was put down, when Magpie miners broke through to Maypitt Mine in what both claimed as their own vein. In such a case the title depended on who had freed the vein first: Magpie freed it the day after the break-through, but Maypitt had worked the veins since about 1740 or even before, and the local Barmoot Jury ruled the vein was indeed Maypitt. Despite this, in two actions in the Barmoot Court, with a special 'independent' jury, the title of the vein was given to Magpie, mainly on the grounds that written proof of freeing must be given to the Court. It was perhaps a coincidence that the previous Barmaster, who had charge of the records, was a Magpie shareholder, though mining records in general in the eighteenth century were poorly kept.

The Maypitt Miners, who also worked the adjacent Great Redsoil Mine, were thus exceedingly resentful, and it perhaps did not help when Magpie were able, in 1829, to demonstrate conclusively that the vein was not Maypitt's after all and thus lawfully and morally theirs, so that it was doubly unfortunate a short while later when a Magpie-owned cross-vein broke into what was claimed as Great Redsoil Vein, definitely freed long before. It was, however, difficult to demonstrate the vein was 'one and the same' from the surface for either side, and for three years first one side then the other, when they thought advantageous, called in the jury in the hope of a favourable ruling, only to find the other side had placed barriers in their route quite illegally. By 1831 both sides had resorted to violence, with sentries on the surface, and fights underground, and both sides lighting sulphur to drive the other out: the inevitable happened in 1833, with three Great Redsoil miners suffocated, and others injured, by the sulphurous fumes, created by Magpie.

At the trial 24 Magpie miners were arraigned at Derby Assizes in May, 1834. Magpie, again advised by Brittlebank, published a 'Defence of the Magpie Miners' as the accused were not allowed to be witnesses in their own defence, which suggested, with some justification, that the act was one of self defence, and that the Redsoil Agent had sent his men knowingly or with wilful negligence into a mine full of gas. The Magpie miners were acquitted.

In 1839 the mine was again opened, this time with a new group of shareholders, and with the Great Redsoil taken into the title. The manager was John Taylor, who operated mines in all areas of Britain and as far away as Mexico, under the "Cornish System". No less than 14 Cornishmen came to live in Sheldon, to introduce large scale methods to Derbyshire, together with the Cornish round chimney and round powder house which still survive, and a Cornish 40 inch pumping engine which replaced the earlier Newcomen. The agent's house and smithy also date from this time, as does the strangely out-of-place square chimney: this was then next to a second boiler house, intended eventually for a new engine and shaft which were never built.

Taylor successfully introduced his new regime; he sank the shaft to about 114 fathoms, developed the mine in an economic manner, introduced new improved practices such as cast-steel borers, safety fuse, a steam whimsey for winding, (the house still stands but was later used for a plant engine) and iron-wire rope; he also made drains to conduct surface water. But the enterprise failed when the shaft penetrated a clay bed and the engine was unable to cope with the increased water. His solution of adopting a 70 inch engine, on either a new or the old shaft, was hotly disputed by Wyatt and his supporters who wanted a sough. Both ideas were outvoted by a third group of shareholders who saw the mine as a perpetual drain on their pockets. Appeals to the Duke of Devonshire for support fell on equally deaf ears for he too had lost much on similar ventures.

Several attempts were made to revive the mine over the next 25 years with schemes involving both sough and engine being put forward, but in 1864 the remaining shareholders gave up the idea, and the mine, and it was taken over by John Fairburn, a Sheffield businessman, mine-owner and smelter, who created a new company. In 1868 Fairburn moved a 70 inch engine from his Calver Sough Mine which closed in 1863. He erected it in the house which now dominates the site, and pumped the mine dry—reaping the harvest which Taylor had sown. Over 850 tons of ore were raised in 1871.

Prospects at greater depth must have seemed bright, but even this engine was incapable of this and in 1873 construction of the Magpie Sough started. It was a financially disastrous, though technically successful venture, draining the mine to about 575 feet below collar, serving as a pump way for water pumped from greater depths. Completion was not until 1881, by which time the engine had been severely damaged in a fire, and the route of the sough proved to be in "Toadstone", hardest and most tenacious of all Derbyshire rocks, for half its distance, stimulating the use of nitroglycerine explosives and pneumatic drills for the first time in Derbyshire but straining the reserves and patience of shareholders, and putting Fairburn deeply in debt. Throughout this period lead prices were falling from the high levels of 1870-71. In 1872 all work at the mine ceased and from 3rd March, 1873 work was

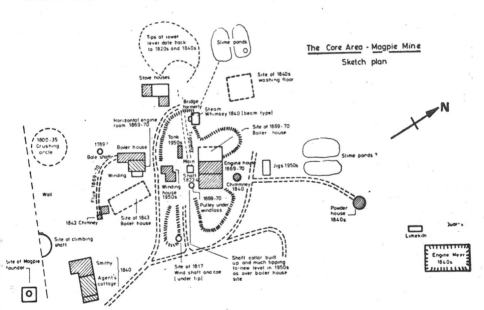

A plan of the surface buildings at Magpie Mine.

61

concentrated on the sough, probably the last of the major soughs to be built in Derbyshire.

In 1874 a water wheel was fixed near the mouth of the sough to power an air compressor to operate a rock drill and to ventilate the sough while it was being driven.

A contract for drilling was made with Richard Schram but after four months trial his compressed air machines and system of working were a failure. The contract was ended and the Company bought the three machines for £250 and worked them in the level using their own men, a method which proved quite satisfactory. The Schram drill was a percussive drill normally driven by compressed air.

By 1879 the sough had reached to beneath Sheldon village, near the point where this excursion commenced. In this year the soughers met an immense quantity of water in powerful springs, and they considered that there was a definite connection with the water in the mine, particularly by draining water from just below the 80 fathom level. It is stated that these springs were met at the crossing of the Townend Vein below the incomplete Sheldon Shaft. This shaft was intended for air and haulage but was abandoned far above sough level after being sunk, firstly through limestone and then about 138 ft. in toadstone.

The sough continued following closely the route of the footpath from Sheldon village and occasionally cutting through mineral veins. As the sough approached the shaft there appears to have been considerable excitement and indeed not a little

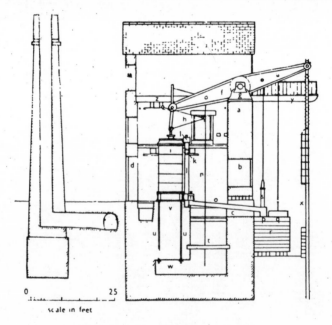

scale in feet

THE MAGPIE ENGINE HOUSE

A cut-away diagram of the Magpie Mine Engine in the 1870's (by V. Roche).

62

danger for the mine itself was now, of course, filled with water. A local newspaper reported 'The tapping of water into the level has been attended with considerable danger, for although the level has from time to time let some of the water down in the mine, yet there was at the time it was cut 108 ft. head of water above them and this would give a pressure of over 55 lbs. to the square inch. As a precaution a long hole was kept in advance of the forefield but if by any chance the shots had penetrated to the water and made a hole one foot square, some of the men would probably have been drowned, for although a hole no longer than a man's had was made first, it had the effect of driving the men forward before the water with great force, putting out their lights and causing them to have to grope their way out in the dark as fast as they possibly could, the water following them at considerable speed'.

This event occurred on 18th August, 1881, over eight years after the sough had been commenced and according to the *Mining Journal* 19th September, 1881, "the event was duly celebrated by a dinner to the workmen on Saturday last". The 'Journal' later states "An outlay of something like £18,000 to clear the water and prevent its further accumulation was certainly a bold venture". Whilst the correspondent gave £18,000 as the cost, the original labour cost was £8,000 and other sources give the actual cost at figures varying from £14,000 to £35,000.

If time permits, a visit can be made to the sough tail (179.696) at the end of this excursion. It may be reached either by a footpath down Nettler Dale, or by turning left (west) along the river bank from the bridge at the foot of Kirk Dale, near Ashford, and following the south bank of the River Wye upstream a distance of half a mile on foot. The sough itself became blocked when an air and winding shaft near the tail partially collapsed into the sough, about 1962. Water accumulated in the mine behind the run-in and after heavy rain, early in April, 1966, water was seen gushing out from several places in the hillside above the sough tail, indicative of the great hydrostatic pressure being produced. On Saturday, 23rd April, 1966 the water burst out of the run-in shaft, blowing a crater some 30 ft. deep and leaving only the bottom 30 ft. or so of shaft which was in toadstone. Several hundred tons of shale and scree were moved, a footpath was swept away and the River Wye partially blocked. The blockage was removed by excavator and the sough re-opened by the Peak District Mines Historical Society in 1974. Wading partly waist deep, for over a mile now provides access to the shaft bottom and a limited stretch of workings at the 92 fathom level. The Blende Vein cavern and workings with their interesting mineral deposits are also accessible from the sough.

While the mine was being prepared for re-opening in 1881 the engine house was destroyed by fire, but by 1882 the main shaft was deepened from 684 ft. to 728 ft.; an operation which could only have been accomplished with a pumping engine raising water to the sough level at 579 ft. But despite impressive reports, including one 'of a seam of blende 5 ft. wide', mining operations ceased in 1883 and a trustee was soon appointed to liquidate the mine. In October, 1883, it was stated "the removal of the engine will, it is believed, entail an expense of not less than £150" and in November, 1883 "The immense pumping engine and fittings which weigh about 300 tons have during the present week been removed from the Magpie Mine at Sheldon to the Manvers Colliery, Stanton Gate. One of the beams in the pumping apparatus was so weighty that it dislodged the crane at Bakewell Station, and some of the fittings are so lengthy that they reached over four railway timber trucks".

Except for the small buildings of corrugated sheet steel, the layout of the mine was at this time much as it is today. The building adjoining the blacksmith's shop had been converted into a dwelling house, and the small lean-to building near the gate was the weigh-house. The whimsey engine house and the round powder magazine date from about 1840 while the orehouse was built about 1869. Together they are typical of any large metal mine of this date in Britain.

The Cornish engine house remains together with the miners' 'dry' (a warm room for changing) on one side and the boiler house, now completely obliterated, on the other. Ore-washing facilities throughout this period remain something of a mystery; the irregular depression near the long engine house was probably a crushing circle used in the 1820s and 1830s. In the 1840s a new floor was built with ore-hoppers and washing grates served by an iron tramway and a hand crushing machine, sieves and buddles by the orehouse. In this area there is still a hillock where traces of a building and slime ponds can be discerned. Water from the pump was sent down the fields on wooden launders to the Magpie drain.

For the 20 years prior to 1906 all the operations at Magpie were on a small scale employing only half-a-dozen men. To get to their working places on the various levels the men climbed climbing shafts, on dressed stones protruding from each side of the shaft in turn. As there was no pump the mine would be flooded to sough level but above this level it would be fairly dry and comfortable. The winding engine remained but which, if either, of two companies recorded as working the mine operated it is not known. How two companies could work the same mine is a mystery, but as there are at least twenty open shafts on the property they were probably not using the same shafts. It is also possible that, as local tradition has it, one of the companies floated the ore in a boat through the sough. This boat is said to have been 23-24 ft. in length, 4 ft. wide, with a capacity of 45-50 cwts. of ore and to have cost £24 to make.

In 1907 the Magpie Mining Company was reformed by E. Garlick and started work in a larger way but still never employing more than twelve men, of whom no more than ten were below ground. In the first five years the mine produced over 5 tons of lead ore yearly and in 1909 and 1910 some zinc also, but at this time the number of men employed was falling rapidly. About 1913 a new company was formed by E. Garlick, combining the interests of both Magpie and True Blue Mines. Work started with seven men, six below ground, and one on surface.

The winder was "Wingy" or "Oud one-arm" Brocklehurst, who it is believed was the person of the same name, formerly the agent for the mine. Captain Moody was the underground manager and Benjamin Handley his mate. A large Lancashire boiler was put in on the surface for the winding engine and another underground

64

for the Tangye (pulsometer) pumps. Two large pipes were fixed up the shaft, one to raise pumped water for the surface boiler and the other for steam. Also a large 'tub' or tank was hitched on to the bottom of the cage to draw water up the shaft for the dressing floors. The cage was also used for winding men and ore but often the men climbed the ladder shafts. Holes were drilled with a hand-drill. On the surface the ore had very little treatment; it was washed, passed through a jaw crusher and then through a couple of hand jigs or hotches. The quantity of water flowing through the sough at the time is said to have been about 8,000 gallons per minute. In 1919 the mine closed once more, the closure being caused partly by shortage of coal during the strike of coal miners in the neighbouring coalfields.

In 1923 Garlick re-opened Magpie employing a total of five men. However, one year later, the company went into voluntary liquidation.

Very little remains of this period mainly because it was a period of make-do-and-mend.

The mine went into its longest quiet spell in nearly 150 years but it was not forgotten and on a number of occasions was visited by geologists, mining engineers and speleologists. One group in 1929 recorded a flow of 8-9½ million gallons of water per day from the sough at an average temperature of 49·5°F, another group in 1937 attempted to reopen the mine but failed. A third group about 1946 entered by means of a sough, and it is recorded, saw a 'ghost'.

In 1951 Waihi Investment and Development Ltd., a London concern, commenced to drain the mine below sough level using electric submersible pumps. An electric winder was put into position on the opposite side of the shaft to the old Cornish engine house and a new cóllar was formed using debris from the mine. The wooden headgear was replaced by a steel headgear and the steam whimsey sold for scrap. Corrugated sheeting was used for the engine house and jig-house, making a strong contrast when seen alongside the earlier stone buildings.

By 1953 the workings had been pumped dry to 620 ft. although in reality water dripped from every crack in the limestone and brownish mud was everywhere. Chatsworth Cavern and Devil's Hole, two large partly natural caverns near the shaft, became accessible but proved disappointing. By 1958 the battle with the water had been lost and with falling lead prices the attempt to reopen the mine was abandoned. Much of the equipment belonging to this period remains *in situ* and can still be seen.

Derbyshire Stone Limited, owners of the Riber Mine at Matlock, the last big lead mining venture in Derbyshire, took over the Title of the mine in 1961 but as yet (1975) no further mining has been undertaken. In the following year the Peak District Mines Historical Society took over the tenancy of the Mine cottage as a field centre, and a base for their study of mining antiquities. On 24th April 1967 a fire occurred at the cottage which completely gutted the building. This occurred in the middle of the night and, because of the isolated position and the dryness of the old timbers of the cottage, the place was well alight before the Fire Service was notified.

Magpie Mine is a living museum, a place which promises rich rewards but where each attempt to exploit it is thwarted by unseen difficulties and each attempt leaves some evidence of its age. Perhaps the curse cast on the mine by the widows of the Red Soil miners in 1833 still stands!

Magpie Mine has such a fascinating history that it tends to make one ignore the other mines in the area and each of these has at one time or another been affected by the developments at their more famous neighbour.

Leaving the mine by the main gate and following the private road southwards, further evidence of mining is very apparent. After about 150 yards Shuttlebank Vein can be seen clearly with its line of subsided ground and frequent open shafts, the largest of which is to be found in the small copse to the east of the track. In this copse there is also the remains of a large gin circle and a raised tramway leads in the direction of Magpie Mine.

The private road leads on to the Ashford-Monyash road and this should be followed in an easterly direction for a quarter of a mile. At the first road junction, the left hand road leads down Kirk Dale towards Ashford. After 200 yards the remains of Mogshaw Mine can be seen to the right.

Mogshaw Mine: (183.679) is on Mogshaw Rake, which, in turn, appears to be a continuation of the Shuttlebank Vein. The mine is very old and has been known as Mockshaw Mine and Haredale Mine, in addition to the more recent 'Mogshaw' Mine.

In 1768 the 'Partners of Haredale Mine' were given 54 meers on "Mogshaw Old Rake", and also 23 meers in Haredale Vein ranging south-east from their 'New Engine Shaft'. This 'engine' is likely to have been a horse-gin since such a gin is shown on an engine shaft 97 yards deep on a mine section dated 1840. Farey in 1811 recorded 'Mockshaw or Haredale Mine, North-west of Bakewell, shale-limestone and first limestone, lead, toadstone, claywayboards'. The latter comments meant that toadstone was present in the workings and that clay intersected the lead vein. The vein was drained in the mid 19th century by a level opening into a swallow hole underground. The mine was worked intermittently throughout the 19th century at one time in the 1840s by George Stephenson of railway fame. It was never an easy mine to work, partly because of the clay already mentioned. As late as 1889 a miner was killed in a roof fall when trying to drive a level through 'old man's' workings at the mine. In later years the mine was owned by Joseph Smith of Youlgreave producing mainly barytes with some lead ore and 'offal' and in the late 1890s it was worked by G. Thompson of Bakewell. The mine was re-opened by the Middleton Mining Company in the immediate post-war years for barytes. Only a little work was done below ground, the bulk of the mineral being obtained from the surface tips. Little remains however of the earlier working as the mined area has suffered the ravages of extensive open cast working in recent years.

Two hundred yards further down the Kirkdale road, on the left-hand side the entrance to a narrow high walled lane can be seen. This is True Blue Lane and, if followed, it leads to the old True Blue Mine.

True Blue Mine: (178.680).This mine is not so deep as Magpie. The foot of the 300 ft. shaft is in toadstone, but workings from the nearby Magpie Mine have penetrated this toadstone and an attempt was once made to drive a raise (an upward shaft) from the deeper Magpie workings below True Blue Mine to the foot of this shaft. It was worked by Benjamin Brushfield in the 1820s and up to about 1841: he spent over £1,000 to deepen it an effort to reach the same depths as Magpie Mine, failed and it was sold to Magpie in 1842 for £200.

The mine was worked in the latter half of the 19th century by George Goodwin of Monyash and many of the buildings, the remains of which can still be seen, date from this period. The mine was taken over in 1913 by E. Garlick, and worked, with Magpie Mine, as the Magpie and True Blue United Mining Co. The mine was, however, never very productive. Returning down the lane to the Kirk Dale Road,

66

follow it downhill until the left fork to Sheldon is reached. At the top of the first short hill on the Sheldon road, Kirk Dale Mine, can be seen to the right.

Kirk Dale Mine: (182.688). There is no mention of this mine in Farey's list of 1811 but the vein was certainly being worked in 1820 and, by 1841, the mine was owned by William Wyatt, the local mine agent, as part of the Fieldgrove Title. The extensive spoil heaps indicate that the mine was worked for some years, but it had certainly been abandoned before 1870. The mine hillocks are at present being reworked for fluorspar and amongst the spoil some excellent geological specimens may be seen, including galena, barytes, fluorspar, calcite and toadstone. From Kirk Dale Mine the road may be followed back to Sheldon village. Fieldgrove Mine is reached by taking the first right hand turn in the village past Sheldon Church.

Fieldgrove Mine: (173.693) is situated on a vein running from Kirk Dale to Deep Dale. The mine has variously been called Field Grove, Field Groove, Field Rake and Sheldon Field.

Farey in 1811 recorded 'Field Rake Mine, Sheldon, first limestone, lead, very wide in spar', and obviously considered it a very profitable working. In 1828 the mine was dispossessed for 'want of workmanship' and given to Richard Holme. Holme sold it to William Wyatt in 1840 who worked this mine together with most of the other mines already described. Shortly after Wyatt took over the mine he sank the main engine shaft and it is obvious that from the start he also had in mind driving a drainage sough from the River Wye. This sough was also intended to go to Magpie and Hardrake Mines. By 1846 the shaft was 462 ft. deep and the workings were much troubled with water and in 1846 the workings were nearly 500 ft. deep, the water problem being very acute. Despite the water difficulties, however, lead ore worth £1,703 was raised between 1840 and 1857 but at a cost of £5,214.

After Wyatt's death in 1858 the mine appears to have been managed by Herbert Milnes of Matlock and it continued to be worked at least until 1860. However by the time the Magpie Sough was being driven in the 1870s, which could have considerably relieved Fieldgrove's water problem, the mine had been abandoned.

The shaft furthest from Sheldon has, nearby, a climbing shaft, a gin circle and a tall windowless building.

Nearer Sheldon there is a large shaft now covered by a mound of limestone blocks and nearby are the remains of a further gin circle and more mine buildings. This shaft is the one sunk by Wyatt in the early 1840's. The gin circle is 42 ft. in diameter and has a centre stone with a 4½ inch square hole, which must have served as a pivot. A horse gin, probably this one, was bought in 1841 for £51, together with some metal air pipes costing £28. Following this visit the return journey must be made back to Sheldon, although should it be desired that the excursion be extended, it is possible to follow public footpaths through Shacklow Woods to the Magpie Sough Tail, a distance of about ½ mile.

5. The Ashford Black Marble Mines and Mill

Conveniently situated so as to be included in a visit to the Sheldon area, the Black Marble mines of Ashford-in-the-Water may also be visited. Cars may be parked at the foot of Kirk Dale, whence the mines may be seen within a walking distance of only a quarter of a mile. Close to the junction of the Sheldon Road and the A6 main road, is the Arrock Quarry (191.694). From here the thin dark fine-grained limestone beds were quarried and taken across the road to the marble mill (190.695) where they were sawn, ground and polished to a fine black surface. The Marble Mill was established on the north bank of the River Wye by Henry Watson in 1748, who used water-wheels to power the marble-cutting machinery. The mill was in use until 1905, since when it has been used as a barytes mill and a lumber yard. Recently most of the surviving mill has been demolished, partly for road-making, and partly to provide storage for the Trent River Board's pipes, etc. but scraps of sawn marble may still be found in the river bed.

The Black Marble was inlaid with coloured stones in geometrical and floral designs as a "cottage industry" in Ashford-in-the-Water and many samples of this dead craft survive in local and national collections. The peak of the trade was in Victorian times, and the demand led to underground mining for black marble both from the Arrock Quarry and in the Rookery Plantation across the valley. Some mine workings are still accessible, particularly in the Rookery. In common with all old mine workings they should not be entered by the in-experienced or without reliable lighting.

A banded brown and grey limestone, known as Rosewood Marble, was worked in Nettler Dale, not far from the Magpie Sough tail, but the relics are now very overgrown. When deeply weathered the black marble beds give rise to "rottenstone". This light powdery stone was used in the 18th century as a fine abrasive in polishing brass, etc. Samples may occasionally be found in the open cuts on Mogshaw Rake or in the fields near Dirtlow Farm.

Chert, used in grinding china-clay, has also been mined near Ashford, but there are more extensive chert mines near Bakewell.

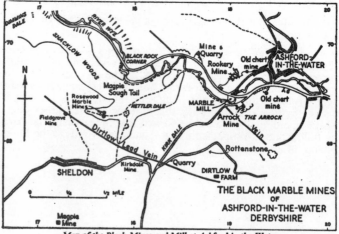

Map of the Black Mines and Mill at Ashford-in-the-Water.

68

6. The Lathkill Dale Mines

2½ inches: 1 mile Map SK 16; 6 inches: 1 mile Maps SK 16 NE & SK 26 NW.
Walking distance either 3½ or 6 miles according to return route.

A great deal of work was undertaken in this area by the old miners, and the Dale is particularly interesting in the unusual layout of the watercourses and aqueducts constructed to provide power to drive water wheels for pumping purposes. The River Lathkill was harnessed and a portion of its water used to drive at least three water wheels, one of which was no less than 52 feet in diameter. Steam power was also utilised and the Dale vividly illustrates the miners' ceaseless struggle with their major enemy—water. Some of the workings are still accessible but **should not be entered by the inexperienced.**

Map of the veins and mines of Lathkill Dale.

Cars may be conveniently parked in Over Haddon village, or alternatively half way down the steep approach road to the Dale. Care should be taken that space is available at the latter, as it is a very popular area at weekends. Two possible routes are included with walking distances of either approximately 3½ miles or 6 miles.

Proceed down the steep access road to the Dale itself. Nestling in the valley floor is Lathkill Lodge (203.661), and a footbridge leads over the river and up through Meadow Place Wood, to a farm from which the wood takes its name. This was once a monastic settlement, so too were the nearby Conksbury Grange and One Ash Grange, the latter being where John Bright, the famous 19th century Birmingham politician, spent his honeymoon.

Do not cross the footbridge, but turn left over a stile and follow the river downstream. Within a short distance the path begins to rise above the level of the river, and here on the river side is disturbed ground which marks the site of the **Lathkill Dale Sough,** and a trickle of water comes from the collapsed sough tail (205.661), close to the impressive Bubble Springs where the main flow of the River Lathkill finally emerges into daylight.

69

The history of the Lathkill Dale Sough will be noted later. Retracing the route back towards the Lodge inconspicuous mounds, now grassed over, mark the positions of shafts sunk along the line of the sough. Formerly there was a shaft in the garden of the Lodge, but this is now covered over, a hand pump marking the site. The sough alters direction here and passes beneath the river at the footbridge. The Lathkill Dale Vein and Sough range in a general south westerly direction through Meadow Place Wood, though surface features are not easily traced in the tangle of undergrowth and trees. (Meadow Place Wood is now a Nature Reserve). ·

Proceeding westwards on the footpath along the north bank of the river, two small trial levels can be seen by the side of the path, neither penetrating the hillside for more than a few yards. On entering the wood some 500 yards west of the Lodge, a partly flooded level can be seen running beneath the path. This is the outfall or tail of **Mandale Sough** (197.661) extending over a mile into the hill, and driven mainly between the years 1797 and 1820, though subsequently extended. The group of derelict mine buildings which can now be seen through the trees to the right were associated with the **Mandale Mine,** where there were large scale efforts during the mid 19th century to pump the lower workings free of water. This mine is reputedly one of the oldest in Derbyshire, and was certainly being worked by the 13th century.

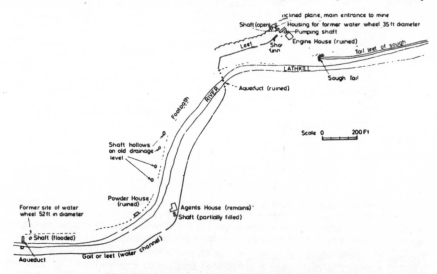

Plan of surface remains at Mandale and Lathkill Dale Mines.

The largest of the remaining structures belongs to the former Mandale Mine Engine House, although it is in very poor condition, being roofless, and only the 'bob' wall being complete enough to permit the former position of the machinery to be ascertained. Behind this is the hollow which housed the water wheel. The pumping shaft, now filled in, was in the bottom of the hollow. Unfortunately a great deal of limestone rubble has accumulated and the top of the shaft cannot always been seen. Above the water-wheel pit, a limestone cliff is penetrated by the 'inclined plane', now the principal means of access to the workings. This entrance **should not be entered** by inexperienced tourists as some of the old workings are **dangerously**

70

unstable. Above the entrance the vein can be seen, *in situ*, between limestone walls. Outside this entrance is a small shaft, still open, which leads via a short cross cut into the sough. Standing with the inclined plane on one's left hand, and the small shaft immediately in front, a small opening may be seen approximately halfway up the opposite hillside. This is a flue which led from the boiler house (now completely obliterated), to a small chimney, the base of which can be seen a little higher than the flue opening.

The Mandale Mining Company started to drive their sough level in 1797 and after 23 years of toil, with little return for their outlay, discovered a rich body of lead ore, followed by a second one in 1823. The first ore strike brought them a profit of £1,155 during a 26-week period, the second, somewhat smaller one resulting in a profit of £584. The Company was anxious to work the vein below the level of the River Lathkill as they were convinced a large body of lead ore remained, untouched by former miners who had used small hand pumps but could not exploit the vein to their satisfaction. During the year 1839, John Alsop, who was associated with the nearby Lathkill Dale Mine, became Agent to the Mandale Mining Company in succession to William Wager who had held the post since 1808. A water-wheel was installed in 1840, and this pumped from a depth of 90 feet below the sough. The wheel was of approximately 35 feet diameter, and the pumps were 14 inches diameter. In 1847 the mine was still in serious difficulties with water, and having two important levels below the sough, it was decided to install a steam engine. The engine house was constructed of limestone quarried a little higher up the dale. The engine itself was constructed on the Cornish principle at the Milton Ironworks, Elsecar. The cylinder was 65 inches in diameter and the engine developed 165 horsepower. This engine was planned to pump from a depth of 160 feet below the river, but it is extremely doubtful if the pumping shaft ever went deeper than the 90 ft. level. The Mandale Mine ceased work in 1851, after it is said, a loss of £36,000. The engine and boilers were removed in 1852, and there is a tradition that one of the pumping machines, possibly the wheel, was removed to Calver Sough Mine.

Returning to the path and proceeding westwards, following the river, the remaining pillars of an aqueduct are soon seen, crossing both the river and the path. Formerly a wooden trough conveyed the water across the tops of the supporting limestone pillars on its way to Mandale wheel. Despite local traditions, the aqueduct was not built in 1810, although a dressed stone bearing that date used to be fixed to one of the pillars. In fact, the date of the aqueduct and consequently the date of the stone is 1840, but obviously the date stone has been defaced at some time and the '4' converted to '1'. There is a small clearing at this point, but within a short distance the path again enters woodland. To the right of the path, large hollows can be seen, and in wet weather a large volume of water overflows from the river into them. They mark the line of an old un-named drainage sough which drained the shallow parts of that Lathkill Dale Vein.

Shortly, a ruined building can be seen across on the south bank of the river; this is generally referred to as 'Bateman's House' (194.658). James Bateman was the Agent to the Lathkill Dale Mining Company from 1836 until the closure of the mine in 1842. Two large shafts, one immediately beneath the house, are nowadays generally known as 'Bateman's Shafts' their correct name not being known. These shafts were the site of a unique pumping engine designed by the Dakeyne brothers, flax spinners of Darley Dale. This was described as a 'disc engine', but in reality was a primitive form of turbine. The mode of operation was very complex, and the various attempts to describe its mechanical complexities are themselves extremely difficult

71

to follow. The main parts of the engine, or perhaps all of it were made at the Adelphi Foundry, Chesterfield in 1831. A reference dated 1833 states that the engine was working satisfactorily at that time. A head of 66 feet of water was used to supply power to the disc and a description states that 130 horse-power was developed. Here the Lathkill Dale Vein, which has ranged through Meadow Place Wood and the fields above, plunges steeply down the hillside, and cuts across the river opposite Bateman's House. The Lathkill Dale Sough runs along the sole (=lowest accessible level) of the vein, and during the extreme drought of 1959 was explored for a distance of approximately 500 yards downstream from beneath the House. Deep water halted progress in this direction, whilst upstream the sough was found to have been bricked up on the north side of the river. Locally, it is said that this was done after the mines were abandoned in an effort to prevent the river sinking into the sough and mine workings and thus losing a large supply of water to Over Haddon Mill. One reference says the bricking up was done in 1854.

The Lathkill Dale Vein was worked from at least 1770 to 1776 by the London Lead Company, who were possibly responsible for the driving of a part at least of the Lathkill Dale Sough. There is also some evidence to suggest that they may also have had a water-wheel working during this time, situated approximately on the site of the later 52 ft. diameter wheel. A plan, drawn in 1826, refers to "where the old engine stood", and shows a surface water course leading from a point higher up the river to this position, with the old drainage level, previously mentioned, possibly taking the pumped water away. The London Lead Company gave up working the Lathkill mines about 1776, and from that date little work was done until 1825, although in 1779 the Hill Carr Sough partners took title to several veins in and near to Lathkill Dale. The Hill Carr Sough at this time had not even reached mines south east of Alport, and never came anywhere near to Lathkill Dale.

In 1825, John Alsop and Thomas Bateman bought a part of the Lathkill Dale Vein for £25 and from then until 1842, the mine was worked on a fairly large scale. John Alsop was a lead smelter and had shares in several other Derbyshire lead mines. In 1830 a lease was obtained from Lord Melbourne to take water from the River Lathkill to turn a water-wheel, but the large wheel was not erected until 1836, but certainly one, if not two, other wheels operated on the mine. The large wheel was 52 feet diameter, 9 feet on the breast and said to be the "largest but one in the Kingdom". Certainly it was a colossal piece of machinery, working six sets of pumps, eighteen inches diameter, and said to be capable of raising 4,000 gallons of water per minute from a depth of twenty fathoms. An interesting facet is that Richard Page an engineer with the Alport Mining Company, was paid £30 "for his attendance and planning from the commencement". This appears to indicate that Page was brought in to advise whilst the wheel was erected and put into operation. By 1832 John Sheldon was the Agent, but he died in 1836 and was succeeded by James Bateman who remained as Agent until the mine closed in 1842. The wheel was offered for sale along with other mining equipment in 1849 but its fate is not known.

On the north side of the river, a little beyond Bateman's House, a small ruined building is all that is left of the Powder House. Shaft-hallows now become prominent, first on the north side of the path, and later between it and the river. These hollows mark the surface course of the Lathkill Dale Vein. The site of the large water-wheel is 290 yards west of Bateman's House, but little can be seen save a portion of the breast walling and a large water-filled hollow. The pillar of a small aqueduct can be seen on the river side, on the opposite bank, with its counterpart on the north side.

During the winter months when the undergrowth is sparse, the leet or artificial channel which conveyed the water to the wheels is well seen on the other side of the river.

Proceeding westwardly 590 yards beyond the water-wheel installation a well-defined vein can be seen ranging north-westwards out of Lathkill Dale Vein up the wooded hillside on the right. This is **Gank Hole Vein** (186.658), or Gank Holes Ochre Mine, worked during the 1880's as a lead and ironstone mine. At this time it had been planned to drive a long level from the Lathkill up this vein, along Mycross Vein and into the Great Greensward Mine, but the project did not live up to the early promise and was abandoned. The level was to act as both drawing gate and sough. Locally it is always said that Greensward Mine and Rake was very rich. About 100 yards east of the Grank Hole intersection is the approximate position of the Lathkill Dale Sough forefield shaft as it stood in 1782. No evidence has come to light to suggest that this level was ever extended beyond this point, but there is a possibility that a branch level was driven up the Sideway Vein by the London Lead Company, and definitely a branch level referred to as the Mandale and Lathkill Company's Deep Level was driven partway up the Mandale Vein, but no distances are known. The pathway emerges from the wood at the site of **Carters Mill** (184.657) and here the excursion can be continued in one of two different ways. For a short return route turn right up the dry side valley on to the minor road which on turning right leads back to Over Haddon village. Just before a junction with the road from Monyash, notice the hillocks and much worked ground of Mandale Rake (190.664). This extends both sides of the road, south-east towards Lathkill Dale, where it has already been noticed, and north-west towards Haddon Grove Farm.

Should the longer alternative route be preferred, continue along the path up the Dale, past a waterfall over calcareous tufa. The Dale curves right slightly and within a short distance, the remains of a coe and small, partially run-in level at the base of a scree slope mark the site of **Smallpenny Vein Sough** tail (180.658). This was recorded in 1814, and the vein can be traced up the steep hillside by narrow workings, none of which are now accessible, and then by lines of grassed-over hillocks, through the fields to the Bakewell-Monyash road. Beyond this point the Dale becomes much rougher. Soon, Cales Dale is seen joing from the south side, and 260 yards beyond, again on the south bank, another partially run-in adit is known as **Holmes Groove** (173.656). It was last worked in the 19th century by a family of Monyash miners of that name. Water often issues from this opening, and the vein crosses the river and can be seen ranging obliquely up the hillside. Further along is the well known and conspicuous cave from which in wet seasons the River Lathkill first emerges into daylight. Some of this water has its source in the Knotlow and Hillocks mines between Monyash and Flagg. The cave is generally known as **Lathkill House Cave** or Lathkill Head Cave (171.659).

The Dale now narrows appreciably and shortly one has to clamber over huge blocks of limestone which appear almost to bar all further progress. Above the blocks to the right is the site of the **Ricklow Quarry** (165.661) from which was obtained the "Derbyshire figured" marble. Geologically, this is not a true marble but a crinoidal limestone, at one time polished and extensively used in ornamental work.

A small mine entrance in a cliff by the quarry was known to old miners as 'Berresford's Cutting' and was started by Monyash miners in an attempt to drain the Magpie Mine on Sheldon Moor. The date 1787 and initials 'I.B.' (Isaac Berresford) are carved at the entrance. The level was not driven very far before it intersected a small natural cavern.

A footpath leads steeply up the hillside a little beyond the mine, and leads to the main Monyash-Bakewell road. At Haddon Grove Farm the hillocks of the Mandale Rake are again seen. Somewhere here was the site of Pasture Shaft and possibly the termination of Mandale Sough. Take the right hand fork, running approximately parallel to the Mandale Rake, and return to Over Haddon village.

7. Hillocks and Knotlow Mines, Monyash

6 inches: 1 Mile Map SK 16 N.W.

These two mines to the northwest of Monyash have extensive workings which can be quite safely visited by experienced and well equipped explorers. Although **access is only possible to experienced parties,** using ladders and ropes, a full description of the undergrounding workings is given so that an impression may be gained of underground features and conditions in Derbyshire lead mines. These two examples exhibit many of the features to be found in medium-sized Derbyshire lead mines. Furthermore they have a fascinating history which has been traced from at least 1702 to the latter half of the 19th century, when the Derbyshire lead industry virtually ceased.

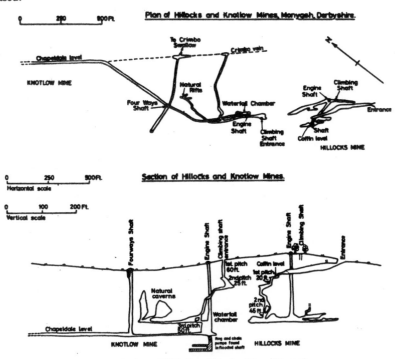

Plan and section of Hillocks and Knotlow Mines, Monyash.

These two neighbouring mines both worked the same two parallel veins, ranging north-west to south-east. Hillocks Mine and the entrance series of the Knotlow Mine were worked in the Whalf Pipe Vein, while the further reaches of the Knotlow Mine were worked in the Crimbo Vein. The original mine documents indicate that the Hillocks Mine also worked the Crimbo Vein, but access to these workings is not now possible. The Whalf Pipe Vein is a complex series of small parallel pipe veins

75

and scrins while the Crimbo Vein appears to be a typical rake vein, even though many documentary references call it a pipe vein. It may be of course that the Crimbo Vein develops into a pipe vein in those parts which are now inaccessible.

Hillocks Mine: Permission to visit Hillocks Mine (and the key) may be obtained from the Derbyshire Caving Association, c/o Sports Council, 26 Musters Road, West Bridgford, Nottingham, NG2 7PL.

Wire ladders and ropes required to visit the lower workings are 1st pitch—35 ft. ladder and lifeline; 2nd pitch—35 ft. ladder, 20 ft. belay and 50 ft. lifeline.

At Hillocks Mine (145.672) one of the Whalf Pipes comes to the surface and this affords the present day access. After stooping through the low entrance, (now gated to prevent vandalism), we enter a roomy passage up to 20 feet wide and 10 feet high. Here traces of mineral can be seen on the roof and walls. When entered by the miners this mineralised cavern was apparently full of broken rocks, calcite, barytes and galena in a matrix of clay and sand with an encrustation of mineral on the walls. Such veins were often very rich and easily worked. Although no positive evidence exists, it is probable that this part of the mine was worked in early times, before the days of explosives.

After about 400 feet, passing under small climbing shafts in the roof and piles of "deads" or waste rock, the roof descends and it is necessary to crawl flat-out through a narrow gap and climb down to the end of a hand-picked level. These levels are met in many old mines throughout Derbyshire. The modern name of "coffin-level" is quite descriptive of the cross sectional shape of many of them—narrow at the bottom, wider at shoulder height, narrow again at the top and just tall enough for a person of medium build to walk along without stooping. Another very distinctive feature is the sweeping pick-marks that bear witness to the fact that these levels were driven without the use of explosives. Gunpowder was first introduced into England for mining from Germany about the year 1670 at Ecton Copper Mines, just 6 miles away. Even so, many of the smaller mines would have continued to use the traditional method of fire-setting to soften the hard, jointless limestone many years after the new techniques were commonplace in the larger mines. This makes it very difficult to date such levels, although they are certainly not Roman. This particular hand-picked level is not of the "coffin" shape, but is only 3 feet 6 inches high and 1 foot 10 inches wide in the centre, being barrel shaped. Proceeding along this passage on hands and knees, the top of a shaft 30 feet deep is reached. This must be descended using wire ladder and rope. This too is of the same hand-picked construction with no signs of shot-holes for gunpowder. These levels and shafts are invariably "gates" or passages from one working vein to another through barren rock. The latter day miner usually calls them "old man's crosscuts".

The shaft reaches into a series of small pipe workings which may be descended with the help of ladders to the lower parts, or "sole" of the mine, 170 feet below the entrance. While descending, dark patches of galena can be seen on the walls, worn smooth by the mud-stained clothing of countless miners and cavers. When working here the miners would have employed "stemples", or stout beams of oak firmly fixed from wall to wall to enable them to climb up and down. In the lower parts of the mine there are large worked-out passages to the left and right. The passage straight ahead enters a waggon gate which was enlarged by the 19th century miners leaving the old man's "coffin" level clearly visible in the roof. This is descriptively recorded in the mine account book for 1844:

76

Benj. Marsden and Part. eight men making a Waggon Road from the (Whalf Mine) Shaft Foot to get into an Old Pipe or Flatt work laying on the West Side of the Whalf Pipe to make the Roof of their Gate at Sole of Old Mans Crosscut and follow a Clay Bed for the Sleepers to rest on. 12 fm. 2 ft. @ £5 15 0 pr. fathom.

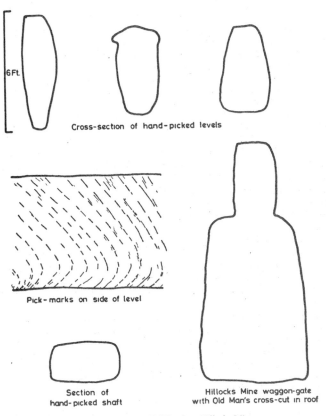

Cross-section of hand-picked levels

Pick-marks on side of level

Section of
hand-picked shaft

Hillocks Mine waggon-gate
with Old Man's cross-cut in roof

Sections of old "coffin" levels at Hillocks Mine.

It seems that this did not justify the effort expended on it and the miners found that most of the lead ore had already been extracted by "T'owd Man". This passage leads to the foot of the engine shaft, 190 feet deep, up which the ore was raised in kibbles, or large wooden buckets, by means of a horse gin. Up till now the air has been quite good, but in these lower parts patches of stale air are now sometimes encountered. This has only occurred since the recent closure of the engine shaft top to prevent vandalism. Prior to this the mine had always been well ventilated; the old miner knew best and always kept as many shafts as possible open to secure a natural draught.

Turning left at the foot of the engine shaft, an extensive series of workings can be explored, while climbing up to the right leads to the base of the climbing shaft—the normal mode of ascent and descent for the working miner. Here the shaft ascends to the surface in 20 to 30 feet stages separated by short horizontal sections. Now only the first few stages can be climbed before progress is halted by a collapse. Downwards to the right leads to a series of "scrins" or small rake veins and eventually to another hand-picked coffin level which is blocked after about 70 feet.

One intriguing feature of this mine is that the 18th century documents clearly indicate that the mine was in serious trouble due to flooding of the workings. By 1740 a sough had been driven to an underground swallow (or natural cavern) to drain the water away. There are many references to pumping, presumably by primitive rag pumps. There is also a possibility of a second, more conventional, sough to "day". Now the modern explorer is less troubled by water. True, it has trickled up his sleeves and he will be very damp and muddy when he reappears at the surface, but there is not enough water to warrant a sough. Where is this water and where are the soughs and swallow? These are some of the fascinating questions which make mine exploration so interesting. Patient exploration, digging and delving into the old mining documents will one day provide the answer.

Knotlow Mine: Permission to descend Knotlow Mine should be obtained from Mr. T. Goodwin, Town End Farm, Monyash.

Tackle required: Entrance Pitch—60 ft. ladder, 80 ft. lifeline; 2nd pitch—25 ft. ladder and 30 ft. lifeline, with belay to foot of First Ladder; 3rd pitch (Waterfall Chamber)—50 ft. ladder, 50 ft. lifeline, 30 ft. belay.

Whereas the present entrance to the Hillocks Mine is not the one the miner would have used to gain access to his lower workings, cavers still use the original climbing shaft when exploring the nearby Knotlow Mine (144.674). The first shaft is a straight 50 feet climb on wire ladder to a small chamber. While descending it may be noted that the top of the shaft is protected from any danger of earth and rocks falling from the top edges by the ginging—a drystone wall lining which extends down until the bed rock is firm and solid.

Provided this ginging does not rest on wooden beams, but on the solid rock, it is often as firm as when it was first built several centuries ago. On opposite sides of the shaft niches can be seen which were to hold the ends of the stemples, which the miner used as a ladder. In other climbing shafts in the area examples can be seen of specially protruding climbing stones in the ginging, or foot-steps cut into the rock walls. Passing under a low arch, a further descent of 25 feet brings us to a natural cavern. Here the first modern explorers to re-enter the old mine found remains of wooden ladders and a series of stemples ascending a wide worked out vein. Since the miners have deserted the mine natural cave formations have started to form, producing small stalactites, rimstone pools and cave pearls. The descent is now through a series of natural chambers, some of which must have been very wide but low bedding plane caves about 4 feet high. These the miners filled with deads, just leaving a narrow passage way through the middle. Eventually this leads to a completely natural and unmineralised series of low passages and very high caverns which the miner never entered. On the way to this natural series a coffin level is passed, which, after twisting about leads to the Crimbo Vein. Here the level is blocked, but water which originates from near the natural series flows down the level, along the Crimbo Vein and is seen again in the lower parts of the mine.

From near the coffin level a further descent leads to the top of a large manmade chamber. From the edge it is possible to look across and see the remains of stemples

78

and a false wooden floor 40 feet above the present floor. After descending the sheer drop using more wire ladders it is seen that the chamber is at the base of a shaft from the surface fully 200 feet deep which ends in a water filled sump. An iron pipe protrudes out of the clear water. From narrow cracks (or bedding planes) high up on the wall of the chamber two streams of water spurt out. This water has been traced to come from the natural section previously noted, and accounts for the current name of Waterfall Chamber. The water standing in the chamber was recently pumped out to reveal workings going down another 40 feet. In them were two rag-and-chain pumps, wooden hand-turned devices which lifted water by means of wads of rags pulled up a hollowed-out wooden pipe. From now on the trip is very wet and any explorer must be prepared for a soaking, which makes him appreciate the awful conditions the miners often had to work in to make a living. Just to the right of the foot of the ladder an inconspicuous opening leads to a fine full height coffin level. This level takes all the water entering the chamber. On proceeding the water becomes deeper until very soon there are only a few inches of air space available. After 500 feet a pile of boulders is reached. These are at the foot of the large Four-ways Shaft down which filters daylight. It is this pile of rocks that has caused the deep water in the level. At the base of the shaft is a large cast-iron bell crank, which was used in conjunction with a small engine on the surface in the 1850s.

Three passages lead off. The right hand branch is another coffin level extending for 300 feet to the Crimbo Vein. Here is a typical rake vein, about 2 to 3 feet wide with the waste rock perched above on wooden stemples. Luckily these deads are quite safe having been cemented together by stalagmitic layers deposited by the seeping water. Here is the remains of what is probably an underground waterwheel erected about 1765 to pump water from the lower workings 60 feet below the level. The water which appears from the bedding planes in the Waterfall Chamber and flows down the level is joined by water flowing down Crimbo Vein and enters a passage which leads to the Crimbo Swallow. This Swallow took the water from the Crimbo Sough as well as that pumped up from the lower workings by the waterwheel. The water eventually re-appears at the Lathkill House Cave, 2 miles away, as the source of the River Lathkill. This is thus an excellent example of the miners' use of natural drainage for the unwatering of their mines.

Returning to the base of the "Four Ways" Shaft, the passage to the left leads to the Whalf Pipe and the base of another large engine shaft. To the north on clambering over stacked deads still awaiting haulage to the surface, a large passage is entered with the remains of truck rails on the floor. After 440 feet the Crimbo Vein is reached and the passage now follows this for a further 1,300 feet. This level is triangular in shape having been cut so as to take advantage of the narrow vein which was being followed. This passage is the Chapeldale Level which was driven from 1832 to 1844 with the intention of draining the Chapeldale Mine at Flagg Town Head, over 1¼ miles away. The miners had hoped that the narrow Crimbo Vein would "belly" out into a rich pipe vein, but their hopes were not fulfilled. Over £6,000 was lost on the project and the level was abandoned with the shot holes still to be fired and the deads to be removed.

On returning to the surface it is possible to appreciate the great battle the miners were fighting with the quantity of water pouring down the level to the Crimbo Swallow. In wet weather the lower levels are completely inaccessible to the explorer, even with his superior equipment and modern lights. It has been known for the water level in the bottom of the mine to rise by nearly 40 feet, nearly to the top of the Waterfall Chamber.

79

8. The Alport-by-Youlgreave Mining Field

2¼ inches: 1 Mile Map SK 26; 6 inches: 1 mile Map SK 26 SW.

A little over 2 miles south of Bakewell stands the hamlet of Alport at the confluence of the rivers Lathkill and Bradford. During its heyday this small area was one of the most intensely worked mining fields in Derbyshire, and owing to its unique geological position, tremendous efforts were made to "unwater" the mines as they went deeper and deeper. Many miles of soughs were driven, with numerous branches following various veins, and waterwheels and a Newcomen engine erected. Subsequently parts of the rivers' flow was diverted down levels and shafts to work water-pressure engines to pump still more water from greater depths. The most interesting facets of the mining story are thus underground, and for the most part inaccessible. The historical introduction to this itinerary will, it is hoped, provide the visitor with a, fascinating background to the surface relics still visible.

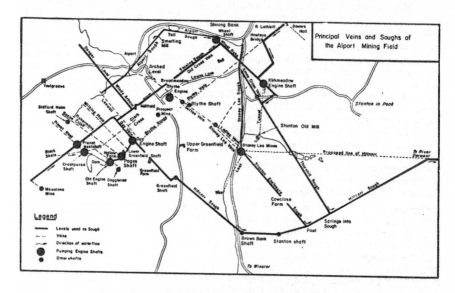

A map of the principal veins and soughs of the Alport Mining Field.

The mines discussed herein lie mostly to the south of the rivers where the limestones containing the veins dip at an angle of about 10° beneath the shales which outcrop only a few hundred feet to the south. These in turn incline beneath the gritstone-capped Stanton Moor. Many of the shafts were sunk in shale to reach limestone at depth. Parts of the soughs were driven in shale too. Two toadstones lie beneath the limestone, and incline southwards from their outcrops around Over Haddon so that they are for the most part far below the mined areas though they were penetrated at depth in Wheel's Rake and in the Mill Close Mine workings well to the south-east

80

of Alport. Toadstone was also reached in Broadmeadow Shaft. The limestone north of the river rises to a little over 600 feet, and to the south-east Stanton Moor rises above the shales to over 1,000 feet.

Hillcarr Sough, the main drainage level for the area, was driven under Stanton Moor into the Alport ground from a point on the west bank of the River Derwent opposite Darley Dale, about 1½ miles south of Great Rowsley. The sough-tail is still open at about 320 feet (258.637). The altitude of the sough in the Alport Mines is probably not much more than 335 feet. Earlier soughs to the River Lathkill provided drainage at about the 400 feet horizon, e.g. Shining and Alport Soughs. The arrival of Hillcarr Sough in this ground thus drained a further 65 feet or so of ground and later provided the hydraulic head to enable the water-pressure engines to drain a further depth of about 125 feet below the sough.

From Long Rake, which lies to the north of the River Lathkill, the strata dip into a trough aligned approximately west to east gently sloping towards the Derwent to the east. The base of the trough runs to the south of the centre of the Alport mining field and appears to form a focal point for the percolating rain water in the surrounding catchment area. Water trickling through the joints and bedding planes of the limestone thus converged to produce a very difficult drainage problem when the pumps installed in these mines depressed the water level below that of the water-table. It was reported when the mines were working that in spite of a certain amount of successful surface work, water still sank into the mines at a rate varying from 2,000 to 6,000 gallons per minute. John Taylor, the famous mining engineer, and manager of Alport Mines in the 1840s expressed the opinion that this was the largest quantity of water ever recorded in the history of mining, though, as he must have known, this was an exaggeration.

Old documents describe the mines as being at the deepest points of a "basin heavily indurated with water". When the pumps were lifting water from below Hillcarr Sough it was at times discharging far more than 6,000 gallons per minute since it was also the outfall for water deliberately diverted down the shafts from the Rivers Lathkill and Bradford to work the hydraulic pumps.

The operation of the pumping engines was thus very much at the mercy of the seasons since during a dry summer or long freeze-up the Bradford and Lathkill provided insufficient water to enable the pumping engines to hold the water level down in the workings.

Mineral Liberties

The mining liberties embracing these veins are Haddon (north and east of the Lathkill), Hartle (=Harthill) (south of the Lathkill and west of Ivy Bar Brook) and Stanton (to the east of the Brook), each with meers of 28 yards, and Youlgreave, (between the Bradford and Lathkill) with 29 yards. All are private liberties.

History

The name Youlgreave appears to be derived from the Saxon Aldgroove or Auldgroove meaning Old Mine. The word 'groove' or grove was commonplace in Derbyshire and miners were often called groovers. The earlies documents and plans which have survived go back little beyond the beginning of the 18th century. The following dates span almost three centuries:

1647 Mineral articles for the Liberty of Harthill written down at a Barmoot Court (confirmed in 1720).

1679 Reference to unsuccessful attempts to unwater a mine at Youlgreave by "wheels and tricks".

1706 Articles of Agreement drawn up to drive Alport Sough, one of several early, shallow drainage levels.

1718 Alport Sough shown on a plan as having reached and being driven south in the Cathole Vein, near Windy Arbour Vein.

1740 Blythe Sough already driven some distance.

c1745 Principal veins taken by a Mr. Haley "from London". He erected a water wheel at Stoney Lee, to lift water to sough level.

c1750 Peter Nightingale drove another sough to Stoney Lee, and erected a 'fire engine' (Newcomen).

1756 Shining Sough started (particularly active in the 1770s).

1756 First reference to Wheel's Rake, previously known as The Sough or Great Vein.

1766 Hillcarr Sough started. It took 21 years to complete and by 1769 it had been driven 1,000 yards in shale.

1774 A gas explosion in Hillcarr Sough injured several men.

1775-6 Relief felt in Stoney Lee as Hillcarr released large springs.

1777 Six men killed by gas in the sough.

1778-9 Stanton Moor Shaft sunk to ventilate sough, so that it could continue. (2,944 yards from entrance).

1780 Brown Bank Shaft sunk to ventilate the sough. (3,358 yards).

1782 Agreement to drive Stanton Enclosure Sough out of Hillcarr to Stoney Lee Mines.

1783 Hillcarr Sough reached Greenfields shaft. (4,218 yards).

1787 First profit for Hillcarr Sough recorded. A celebration was held for the unwatering of Guy Vein. The sough was driven north-west up Guy Vein and north-east up Old Cross Vein to Broadmeadow.

1791 Agreement with Bache Thornhill to drive Thornhill Sough, a branch level, out of Hillcarr Sough.

1801 Richard Trevithick, the well-known Cornish engineer was approached concerning an engine suitable for Alport Mine.

1802 Trevithick submitted drawings of a hydraulic engine.

1805 Trevithick's engine installed at Crash Purse shaft. (It was later moved to 'Old Engine Shaft').

1813 A second, similar but smaller engine erected by Richard Page on Bacon Close Vein.

1819/1820 First hydraulic engine installed at Broadmeadow.

1825 Reference to a water-wheel on Wheel's Rake.

1835 A large water-wheel was installed at Wheel's Rake.

1836 A new engine at Broadmeadow started work.
A new water-wheel at Wheel's Rake was pumping into a further extension of Thornhill Level, made between 1825 and 1835.

1839 Titles of all mines owned by Hillcarr Sough, Shining Sough and Blythe Mines consolidated to form Alport Mining Company.

1841 Tenders for a further hydraulic engine examined. The underground water-course to convey water from the River Lathkill to Guy engine completed.

1842 The main shafts had been sunk 21 fathoms below sough level and main levels had been driven in several veins.

1845 Alport Mining Company order another hydraulic engine for Pienet Nest Shaft.

1847 Serious water trouble was encountered and all engines stood idle for a time.

1848 A hydraulic engine installed on Thornhill Sough in Stanton. Another crisis due to excessive water in the Alport Mines.

1851 Alport Mining Company informed Mr. Thornhill that they would have to abandon Stanton Mines due to water trouble.
By November the engines and other equipment were advertised for sale.

1852 Mine equipment sold by auction.

1854 Final dividend paid by the Alport Mining Company. A 'New Company' was formed by some of the shareholders. Suggestions in the Derby newspapers to extend Hillcarr to Magpie Mine.

1860s Danger Level extension of Hillcarr Sough being driven up Windy Arbour Vein.

1870s Revival of interest in Hillcarr Sough as a means of draining Mawstone Mine.

1875 Alport Mining Company ended active mining, and relied on composition from the sough. Most shareholders withdrew.

1878 Mosstone Mining Company formed to work Mawstone Mine.

1882 Mawstone Level driven along Clay Vein as an extension of Hillcarr Sough.

1891 A steam engine and a ventilation pump were at Mawstone Mine.

1893 Mosstone Mining Company went into liquidation.

1919 Bradford Vale Mining Company Limited of Matlock formed to work Mawstone Mine (would up in 1967). Put forward a scheme to unwater the mine by hydraulic pumps.

1922 A further scheme to extend Hillcarr to Lathkill Dale and Magpie Mines.

1932 Serious gas explosion at Mawstone Mine whilst driving level in shale towards Gratton Dale killed 5 miners and 3 rescuers and thus closed the mine. Underground work was not started again.

1974 Planning permission given for underground mining at Shining Bank, north of the Lathkill-Bradford.

The dates given above serve to put into perspective the rise and decline of mining activity in the Alport field. The story which emerges is one of an industry expanding rapidly in the second half of the 17th century and striving to reach ore beneath the natural water table. During the early 18th century a great deal of effort was expended on dealing with the water problem by driving several soughs from the River Lathkill and Bradford (old maps show seven soughs) and in the late 18th century by driving Hillcarr Sough from the River Derwent. As the miners strove to reach deeper ore the opening of the 19th century saw the development of an extensive drainage system based on the use of water pressure engines utilising Hillcarr Sough as a pumpway. Some of the 18th century soughs and the pumping engines of the 19th century are particularly interesting.

Hillcarr Sough

Started in June 1766 it became the longest sough in Derbyshire with a length of 4½ miles. The major shareholders were smelters and mine owners, Peter Nightingale of Lea, and John Barker of Bakewell. Another was John Gilbert, agent to the Duke of Bridgewater, who had overseen the construction of the underground canal system in the Worsley Coal Mines, and the Bridgewater canal which linked them to Manchester. The Worsley Mines and canal were visited by Barker, and the then advanced technology used in driving the sough was probably derived from coal mining experience via Gilbert. Apart from the unusually large size of the tunnel, up to ten feet before arching, and the use of boats for haulage, fans and a water-blast were used for the air supply, instead of relying on frequent shafts, while boring was introduced to link the shafts to the sough below. The surveying must have been exceptionally good, to intersect shafts so far apart. By 1769 the sough had progressed in a westerly direction about 3,000 feet but then instead of proceeding to Stoney Lee Mines, it turned south-west for about ¾ of a mile, to avoid driving in limestone, keeping in the softer shale in which the Stanton Moor and Brown Bank Shafts were sunk. From Brown Bank it went north-west, reaching Greenfield or Great Shaft in 1783. Close to where Thornhill sough branches north-west, strong springs were encountered and these drained Plackett Mine at Winster, two miles to the south!

The sough was navigable by long flat-bottomed boats as far as Greenfield Shaft. Though it was subsequently to be extended in several veins, the sough was considered as completed in 1787 having reached Guy Vein after taking 21 years to drive and the expenditure of some £32,000. In 1787 the first profits appeared in the Reckoning Book, and are said to have covered the expenditure on the sough within two years of its completion due to the rich ore which it made accessible. Work inside the sough must have been hard and unhealthy in wet conditions with bad air. Airshafts were few, and the explosions show that the fans and waterblast did not entirely overcome the ventilation problems.

The boaters were paid 1/2d. a day whilst the miners and pumpers received 1/- a day. The cost of driving the sough rose from 25/- to 50/- a fathom in 1769 to between £3 and £10 a fathom in 1770 which reflects increasing difficulties rather than rising wages. The wet conditions required the use of tin tubes to enclose the charges of gunpowder for blasting. To keep the sough clear of accumulated mud, men were employed to keep the water and sludge moving by means of primitive churn pumps and scrapers. The men undertaking this wet work were paid around 2/- a day, twice as much as the miners. Little wonder that the masters urged the men in their difficult task with free issues of gunpowder and candles (normally purchased by the men) and gifts of ale, rum, meat and bread. The completion of the sough in 1787 was celebrated in April of that year. The Reckoning Book shows "expenses at the rejoicings" and "bottles of rum to Hillcarr"—£36! An ox and two sheep were roasted and ale was provided by the Duke of Rutland. Some 400 to 500 people attended the celebration in spite of poor weather!

A branch of Hillcarr Sough known as Stanton Enclosure Sough was driven towards Stoney Lee Mines sometime after 1782 and in 1791 an agreement was entered into to drive another sough branching out of Hillcarr Sough and to be known as Thornhill

Sough, later extended along Wheel's Rake to the Wheel Shaft between 1825 and 1835. Suggestions to extend the sough towards Magpie were not taken up, except for the Danger Level, following Windy Arbour Vein under the River Bradford, into Youlgreave Liberty, and the most important nineteenth century extension was the level along Clay Vein to the Mawstone Mine, in 1882.

The Water Pressure Engines

Much of the rich ore which became accessible in 1787 was won during the next decade and thoughts soon turned to deeper drainage. The low gradient of the Derwent made it impractical to drive a sough deeper than Hillcarr. The need therefore arose for a pumping engine. The economics of steam power proved to be unfavourable and the topographical features appeared well suited to the use of water power and the subsequent pumping engines installed in the Alport area were hydraulic, i.e. water pressure engines, except for a water wheel on Wheel's Rake.

The hydraulic engine is designed to make use of a small volume of water with a large fall. The principle of operation is that the piston is moved within the cylinder by water pressure instead of steam. During the 19th century seven such engines were placed underground in the Alport and Stanton Mines, all but one of them powered by water from the Bradford and Lathkill Rivers carried by iron pipes down the shafts. The motion of these engines was carried to pumps by means of pump rods thus lifting water from below Hillcarr Sough and discharging it, together with the water used to work the engines, into the Sough, or its branches.

Negotiations with Richard Trevithick started in 1801 concerning the first engine, subsequently known as the Old Engine or Trevithick Engine. During the 47 years that it worked it saw service in Crash Purse Shaft and later in the shaft near Hollow Farm. It started work in 1805. The water which powered it was carried down the shaft in pipes 15 inches in diameter with a fall of 150 feet, and this high pressure water acted alternately on either side of a piston moving in a cylinder 24 or 25 inches in diameter by means of two valve pistons raised and lowered by a rocking beam. The beam was connected to and moved by the pump rods working two 33 inches diameter pump cylinders with a stroke of 10 feet. Rods in the shaft were connected to a balancing beam at the surface. The engine appears to have worked at about 3 strokes per minute, each stroke using 416 gallons of feed water and raising rather more than 250 gallons from about 50 feet below the sough. It had been designed to work at about twice this rate and develop 174 hp. This engine stayed in service until the closing of the mines in 1852. A second engine, similar in design was installed in 'Pages Shaft' about 1813, by Richard Page who remained as engineer until 1842. But both engines acting together found it hard to cope with the water. In 1819 a third engine, known as the Blythe Engine, was installed in Broadmeadow Shaft.

The fourth engine, a single acting engine made by William Fairbairn of Manchester was installed in Broadmeadow Shaft in 1836. The installation was difficult as the engine base alone wighed over 4 tons and measured about 14 ft. by 6 ft. To transport the beam up Priesthill required 18 horses. Some parts were late in delivery and the reconstruction of the engine in the confined space excavated for it underground presented problems. The installation took from January 1836, when the base was laid, until the following September, but it failed in 1837.

By 1838 it was apparent that future mining required much more pumping power, and to effect this the three main companies in the area consolidated to form the Alport Mining Company, and invited John Taylor to become the manager. As at

Magpie and elsewhere he attempted to introduce the 'Cornish System' of mining on a large scale, and ignoring James Barker's suggestion to install a steam engine, he used hydraulic engines on a lavish scale to deepen the workings from 8 fathoms to about 21 fathoms below the Hillcarr Sough. Old Engine and Blythe Engine shafts were sunk to this level in 1841, whilst, by using an old engine, possibly the 1819 engine, with an 18 inch cylinder and 7 feet stroke, and old shaft, known as Guy's, was widened and deepened, and prepared for the largest of the engines, the famous Guy Engine. This was made by the Butterley Company, and installed by early 1842. This huge engine had a cylinder diameter of 50 inches, with a stroke of 10 feet. Iron pipes carried on a wooden viaduct conducted the feed water from the River Lathkill over Alport village just above Alport Bridge and through a tunnel in the hillside (still open for a few yards) which ran first to Broadmeadow Shaft and then to Guy Shaft. Here the water descended 132 feet in 40 inches diameter iron pipes in the 11 feet 4 inches by 10 feet 4 inches shaft (now only a water-filled hollow). This column of water acting only on the underside of the 50 inches diameter piston exerted a pressure of 58 lbs. per sq. inch representing a force of 50 tons on the piston. The engine was situated 210 feet below the surface and working at about 70% efficiency pumped from a depth of nearly 140 feet below the sough by working, through massive plunger (pump) rods, a 42 inches diameter pump discharging an estimated total volume of about 5,000 gallons per minute into the sough in very wet weather. The rods were of pitch pine two feet square and performed 5 strokes a minute of the plunger. A model may be seen at the South Kensington Science Museum.

By 1845 it was considered necessary to install yet another engine, with twin 24 inch cylinders and 10 feet stroke, on Pienet Nest Shaft, whilst in 1847 a further engine was placed in Kirkmeadow Shaft to drain the Stanton Mines. This was specially made so it could have liners placed inside the cylinders to reduce them from 24 to 19 inches diameter, in order presumably to economise on water, since the streams used were very small, despite long leats and tunnels.

Despite this proliferation of engines however, the water was not overcome. In winter heavy flooding took place, in summer, otherwise the most favourable season, there was an inadequate water supply from the rivers, so that in 1847 Taylor decided in dry seasons only to pump to 10 fathoms depth, instead of 21 fathoms, whilst it was hoped the Stanton Engine would cope with winter inrushes. This was also unsuccessful, and the contemplated 12 fathom level below the sough was abandoned during sinking, and the level went off at 8 fathoms instead. In 1849 and 1850, with long droughts, the mines remained virtually full to sough level, with only a few small trials continuing.

Thus, beset by winter floods and summer droughts, with the veins small and close at depth, and with shareholder confidence declining with falling lead prices and the high costs of the Cornish System, the mine closed and was sold up in 1852, with accumulated losses of over £18,000. Indeed the mine covered its running costs for only a few months of its life, and was both a commercial and technical failure, despite the fame it achieved under Taylor.

A Tour of Present Day Remains — walking distance 4½ miles.

Forking south from the A6 road 2 miles south-east of Bakewell the A.524 road follows the River Lathkill for a mile before reaching Hawleys Bridge (231.648). Turning left at Hawleys Bridge a further 300 yards south along the A.524 road leads to a convenient parking place on the right at the Lawns Lane junction (231.646).

Looking back towards Hawleys Bridge, Priesthill, in Harthill Liberty, rises immediately to the left with a stone-cairn-covered shaft down at road level. Priesthill is crossed by about six SW-NE veins almost equally spaced between this viewpoint and Hawleys Bridge, and several shaft hillocks may be seen, the most important of which are probably on Blythe Vein, ranging from Bowers Hall (235.650) to the Blythe Mine above Broadmeadow (227.642).

Wheel's Rake runs NW-SE close to Lawns Lane junction and at this point we are standing almost above the Thornhill Sough extension of Hillcarr Sough, about 60 feet below road level, and what at one time was Stoney Lee Sough, just below road level and discharging at Hawley's Bridge.

Leaving Lawns Lane junction and going south for about 200 yards on the A.524, take the Stanton-in-Peak road to the left for about 150 yards. Beyond the sharp bend a walled nettle-filled enclosure may be seen immediately to the left of the road (232.643). This is an open shaft on Amos Cross Vein. Some 150 yards across the fields to the north is a tree-ringed raised mound in front of a barn (233.644). In this is an open stone-lined circular shaft some 9 feet in diameter. It is well preserved, in spite of being situated in shale, and bears testimony to the care and skill of the miners in having lined the shaft so well. It is marked on an old plan as Kirkmeadow Shaft and is at the junction of Wheel's Rake with the Thornhill Sough branch of Hillcarr Sough. This shaft housed the Stanton hydraulic engine, which was fed by water via a level about 20 feet down the south wall of the shaft. This level led to the marshy area just downslope, where there was probably a small dam, which accumulated water from the small stream, and from a tunnel driven under the hill to Stanton Old Mill (233.639) which was fed by another small stream, and by a leat extending half a mile to the Ivy Bar Brook.

Thornhill Sough is about 60 feet below the mouth of the shaft. Beyond the shaft a branch from Thornhill Sough extends to the vicinity of Bowers Hall. Returning to the Stanton-in-Peak road a large shaft mound is visible directly across the road on the hillside. Here may be seen another open shaft on Thornhill Sough (233.642).

Retracing our steps to the A.524 and going a further 500 yards south along it we reach a layby on the left where the Brook runs under the road (231.638). A short distance along the track going up the bank encircling the layby is a large hollow. This was the main shaft of the Stoney Lee Mines, (231.637), which in the eighteenth century was the site of a waterwheel, and then a fire engine, which pumped water into soughs constructed for the purpose. The leat, which may have supplied water for the wheel, but which a century later certainly carried it to the Stanton Old Mill, can be seen further down the road, as a vague depression between the road and the Ivy Bar Brook, (230.636) near the milepost, until it reached the Brook at a small weir (229.634) opposite the Lodge.

Hillcarr Sough was originally directed towards the Stoney Lee Mines, but its course was changed and it passed under the A.524 about 800 yards to the south of the layby and communicated with the surface at this point by Brown Bank Shaft immediately adjacent to the east wall of the road (231.630). This shaft was sealed for safety a few years ago. Signs of a spoil heap on the west side of the road mark the place. This was intended to be the first shaft on the west side of the moor, but ventilation problems forced another shaft to be sunk, the Stanton Moor Shaft about 400 yards to the east near Cowclose, (235.630), which ran in during 1973. The Ivy Bar Brook was used for a water blast on Brown Bank Shaft, to ventilate the section to Greenfield Shaft, and for the driving of Stanton Enclosure, and perhaps Thornhill's Soughs.

Returning to the layby, and crossing the road, follow the track north-west up the field along the course of Stoney Lee and Ladies Veins to Sutton Vein, marked by several shaft mounds and open shafts. These veins are crossed by a number of other veins, including Black Shale and Blythe, and were extensively worked from both Stoney Lee and Broadmeadow. Beyond the crest of the hill a plantation is reached, and shortly Lawns Lane is regained at Broadmeadow. The cottages here (224.643) were the offices of the Alport Mining Company, and the Broadmeadow shaft in which the Blythe Engines were placed, is by the cottages, but filled with rubbish. Shining Sough passes under Broadmeadow, and runs diagonally under the gently sloping grazing land. To the left by Broadmeadow Cottages, Lawns Lane meets the Alport to Elton road.

Turning south up the Alport to Elton road from Broadmeadow for about 150 yards a patch of disturbed ground to the right (west) of the road marks the open shaft of Prospect Mine which continued working for some years after the old Alport Company was sold up.

Continuing up the road, Upper Greenfield Farm is passed on the left, and some 300 yards further on the right, a footpath leads to Greenfield Farm, (shown as Lower Greenfield on some O.S. maps). A few yards from the road in the field next to the path is the half-open, but largely rubbish filled top of Greenfield Shaft, reached in 1783. The post of gritstone nearby is very likely one of those laid out to mark the direction of the sough, which from here heads towards Guy Vein, almost under the Greenfield Farmhouse. The track is then followed to Lower Greenfield Farm, behind which a circular wall guards the open shaft in which Richard Page placed his 1813 engine. Further down the field are the buildings of Hollow Farm, with the filled in 'Old Engine Shaft' (219.637), where the earliest of the hydraulic engines worked, after its removal from Crashpurse shaft near the lower end of the dam. Water for these engines, and for the later Pienet Nest Engine was brought from the river via Pienet Nest and Black Shale Veins, and from Hollow Dam. A short distance beyond the farm buildings the cart track reaches a crossroads with another track which is the one running by Millfield Farm and meeting the end of Lawns Lane at Broadmeadow. This track runs through a plantation 150 yards north-east of the crossroads and here is the site of Guy Shaft where the Guy Engine worked (221.639). It ran in many years ago and is now an overgrown depression.

Returning down the track and going beyond the crossroads the track bends to the right towards Youlgreave passing Pienet Nest Shaft (concreted over in 1967) on the right of the track (216.638). From this shaft the Mawston Level extension of Hillcarr Sough runs to Mawstone Mine where an explosion in 1932 killed eight men. The spoil heap of Mawstone Mine is clearly visible a few hundred yards to the south-west. The riverside path to Alport is now taken passing Sidford Holm shaft and several veins which have been worked under the river. Danger Level, an extension of Hillcarr Sough, runs from near Millfield Farm and passes under the river near Rheinstor Rock (219.644) just above Alport and extends under Lathkill Dale. On reaching Alport the low road near the river is taken and a small footbridge (221.645) will be seen crossing the river 120 yards upstream from Alport Bridge. Near the top of the wooded slope reached by this footbridge may be seen the arched level, almost filled with chicken manure, which conveyed water to Guy Shaft via Broadmeadow Shaft to power the hydraulic engines. The level is blocked by a fall a few yards from the entrance. The water was conveyed into this level by iron pipes carried on a viaduct over the River Bradford near the footbridge.

Downstream from Alport Bridge the south bank is in private land, and it is necessary

88

to keep to the road on the north bank. Although it is much overgrown it is still possible to look across at the bend (222.649) and see part of the ruins of an extensive smelting mill on the hillside (223.648). This was one of the principal smelting works of the third quarter of the nineteenth century, and galena from many mines was smelted in two reverberatory and several other types of furnace to produce molten metallic lead cast into 'pigs'.

There are long tunnels running at four levels for over 150 yards along the hillside forming a complex, long flue arrangement to condense the lead fumes arising from the various furnace processes. Long flues were necessary to prevent the escape of lead vapour into the atmosphere on the one hand since this usually resulted in lead poisoning of people, animals and vegetation in the area, and on the other hand, because the lead which was condensed and recovered in this way could represent as much as a twentieth of a mill's output. The flue terminates in a chimney stack 34 feet high on the hillside above the mill. J. Percy in his *Metallurgy of Lead*, 1870, gave detailed drawings of the furnaces and flues and described their operation. The mill ceased working about 1875.

A low drain-like opening by a dam, a short distance downstream (225.649) discharges water which is said to come from Alport Sough. The agreement for driving this is dated 1706. A plan in 1718 shows that by then it had been driven more than half-a-mile to the Cathole Vein by Rheinstor Rock and followed for much of the way a course almost directly beneath the bed of the Lathkill. The original entrance is shown on old plans further downstream near Wheel Shaft.

After a further 300 yards a mound with an arched opening facing away from the river will be seen on the south bank of the river (229.648). This is the Wheel Shaft on Wheel's Rake. The masonry structure in this mound housed a water-wheel working pumps which raised water from the 192 feet deep shaft and discharged it into a level running via Thornhill Sough into Hillcarr Sough. Work here is thought to have stopped in 1851 but in the northward extension of Wheel's Rake across the river, work continued into the 1880s.

For those bent on underground exploration and properly equipped with helmet, old clothes, boots and a reliable lamp, the cleft 5 yards from the mound gives access to over 400 yards of sough-like level which runs towards the sharp bend in the road south-east of Alport, and which may be Shining Sough, though old plans show this latter running to Broadmeadow Shaft. It was driven after 1756, through Broadmeadow for a total distance of about a mile, terminating near Pienet Nest Shaft, and led to considerable mining in the 1770s until Hillcarr replaced it.

On the opposite side of the river to Wheels Rake is Shining Bank behind which runs Long Rake. Further to the west above Alport this is being opencasted, but here planning permission has limited working to underground methods, so that this is perhaps the first stage of the revival of the traditional local mining industry.

Following the river for a further 300 yards Hawleys Bridge is once more reached and a similar distance to the right along the road brings us back to the starting point at Lawns Lane junction.

9. The Matlock and Cromford Area

2½ inches: 1 mile Maps SK 25 & SK 26. 6 inches: 1 mile Maps SK 25 NE and SK 26 SE. Walking distance: 3-6 miles, according to return route.

A convenient point to start this tour is Cromford Market Place, though if an appropriate map is used, several variations are possible starting or finishing at Matlock Bath or Matlock. A full tour will involve a walk of some 5 or 6 miles, and will necessitate some means of transport back to the start. Frequent buses run through the Matlock dale.

Matlock has been traditionally associated with lead-mining since Roman times; in fact some would have it that the Latin inscription LVTVDARVM found on pigs of lead dug up around Matlock, was the name of a Roman mining settlement somewhere near Matlock. Others place this lost Roman village in or near Chesterfield, at Wirksworth, or at some unknown site, possibly Cromford.

The Roman writer Pliny was probably referring to this area in A.D. 79 when he stated "In Britain, in the very upper crust of the ground, lead is dug up in such plenty, that a law was made on purpose to stint them to a set quantity". Roman pigs of lead have been found in the Matlock area, one on Cromford Moor in 1777, weighing 126 lbs., another at Matlock in 1783 weighed 84 lbs., yet another on Matlock Moor in 1787, weighed 173 lbs. Most have a Latin inscription, giving in various abbreviations the metallic district, the merchant and Emperor.

The Saxons also knew and worked this area and yet more recently prisoners taken in battle during the wars with France were put to work in the mines. The Industrial Revolution and later the rise of tourism brought many changes to the Matlock area, but many mining relics are still to be seen, though road-widening and the rebuilding of other properties have made some inconspicuous.

The Manor of Cromford some two hundred years ago would hardly be recognised by anyone in this 20th century. The name itself, once "Cruneford", in early English meaning "crooked ford", derived from the fact that of the streams draining from the valleys to the west, one flowed through the centre of the hamlet to join the river Derwent. Anyone journeying from the south to Matlock had to ford the waters but since 1790, Cromford Market Place, with its culvert beneath, obscures it all. Sir Richard Arkwright obtained the grant of a market and erected the buildings on its northern side, locally called the 'Shambles', the first market day being held on the 19th June, 1790. The A6 road through the Derwent valley was not built until 1818 and on the 4th March, 1795, a labourer employed in getting limestone at Scarthin Nick, which was first cut through at this date, discovered a human skeleton in a cavity and by the head lay over sixty small Roman copper coins in good preservation.

About a mile up the Via Gellia from Cromford, at the top of the steep hillside facing the Pig O' Lead Inn is **Ball Eye Mine** (287.574) and it may be convenient to pay this a visit before starting the main walk. The lead ore, galena, here has the reputation of containing more silver than any other lead in Derbyshire, which is normally considered to be poor in silver. Up to 20 ounces of silver to the ton of lead has been claimed at Ball Eye, though most samples assay much less than this today. Ball Eye Mine is at two levels. High at the top of the slope is the wide open cave entrance, often known as Ruggs Hall, leading to workings with much blue fluorspar, unfortunately too crumbly to use as Blue John. Ruggs Hall was a farm on the hilltop above Ball Eye, but it has now vanished and the name is often applied to the cave, which is now dangerously unstable and sometimes contains fumes. By 1630 the mines here were already quite deep and expensive to drain. Late in the 17th century a mammoth's skull was found in one of the nearby shafts. Lower down the slope, about 100 feet above road level are a number of pipe workings in a mixed ore of barytes and white calcite.

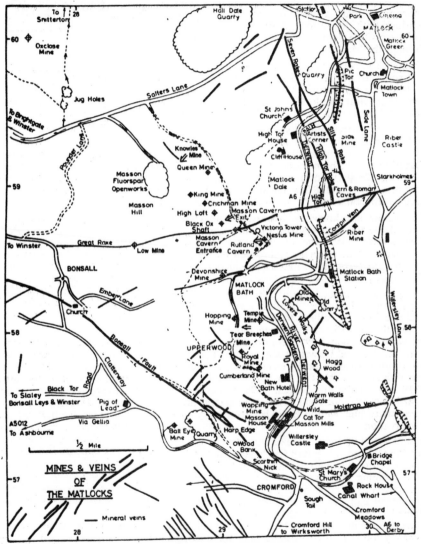

A map of the mines and veins of the Matlock area.

Returning to Cromford Market Place, directly opposite the Via Gellia road, an opening between two shops leads after some 50 yards to a small walled enclosure on the left and in the bottom of this is the *"tail"* to **Cromford Sough** (295.568), also visible near the school in North Street. This was started during the early 1630s but appalling ventilation difficulties were encountered and it was not completed to Gang Vein at Black Rocks until 1709. This section was a mile long and numerous extensions were carried out during the following century.

The sough and branches were completed, at a cost of £30,000, about the time that Sir Richard Arkwright decided upon erecting a cotton mill here so two small dams were made between Derby Road and Mill Lane and the water was fed across the lane passing into the Derwent opposite Willersley Castle.

The water is still conveyed across Mill Lane by the cast iron aqueduct, replacing a timber structure, to enter the Mill of 1771 where it once powered a water wheel.

With the implementation of the Cromford Canal Act of 1789-90 (with amendments in 1791) the surplus water from Cromford was conveyed to feed the Canal and it was said that "due to the temperature of the sough water the canal remained navigable during severe frost".

Subsequently the Meerbrook Sough was driven from the Derwent near What-standwell, to unwater the same mines at an altitude about 100 feet lower, so that the flow through Cromford Sough was considerably reduced. Sir Richard and the soughers had a long drawn-out law-suit in which he unsuccessfully tried to get his water-power restored to its former strength.

Arkwright, Need and Strutt, as partners, erected the first Mill at Cromford on a site in the yard of the present building in the year 1770. It is believed to have been a temporary structure, possibly of wood, for in 1771 the present building was erected without windows in the outer walls of the lower floors to prevent access and damage by vandals who saw the world's first water powered cotton mill as a threat to the local family businesses known as "Stockingers' Shops". It was here in this mill in the year 1773 that calico was first manufactured. Subsequent to the building of Masson Mill, Cromford Mill was disused, later to become a Brewery (Offilers) and many years later, after a disastrous fire, it became a colour factory, continuing to serve this trade to the present time.

Continuing down Mill Lane, on the opposite side of the road, near to the eastern extremity of the Car park, the water supply feeding the Canal is seen flowing into the "Cut" at the Coal Wharf. Within memory coal was delivered to this point by barge and distributed to the surrounding area by horse and cart. The Wharf once had its own stables with a blacksmith's shop and facilities for the repair of barges. With the introduction of the railway through the valley, Matlock Bath Station became the destination for bulk deliveries of coal. The canal came to a halt and the wharf a stock ground for local coal supplies. Eventually the transshipment of coal from rail to cart, later lorry, then the business of storage and reloading for delivery to the customer proved too much and the transportation by rail declined in favour of direct road deliveries. Finally, in 1972, this long established family business closed and the former office, outbuildings, general and grain warehouse were bought by the County Council in the interests of conservation. The yard has already been landscaped to form a car park and picnic area, and the canal is scheduled for recreational facilities.

On the cliff top behind the canal, partly hidden by the trees, stands "Rock House" (299.569), now converted into flats, but once the home of several notable families

92

in years gone by, the Strutts, Curzons and Arkwrights all having resided here for a time.

Across the way, the Church of St. Mary was built upon a site formerly known as the "Green", with its foundations in the refuse slag of an ancient lead smelting furnace.

A weir in the river 50 yards north of the Church gave power for a water wheel to operate bellows for the smelting of lead. This was the eighth weir between Matlock and Cromford, seven of which were built to drive water-wheel pumps to unwater lead mines along the water's edge through the valley.

A water-colour drawing of Old Willersley in 1786 showed the present St. Mary's Church site occupied by Smelting Mills with tall brick chimneys in front of which passed the old road to Matlock Bath. A treacherous footway had long existed along the riverside but when the beneficial properties of the first thermal spring had become widely known, visitors sought to take the waters at Matlock Bath and in the year 1702 a Horseway was constructed. In 1745, having bought the lease of the thermal spring from George Wragg, Messrs Smith and Pennel, two Nottingham gentlemen, constructed a carriageway from the west side of Cromford Bridge to admit visitors safely to their hostelry and Bath-house. This was achieved by widening and improving the horseway of 1702.

The road was finally closed in 1790 when Richard Arkwright junior, objecting to the increasing number of visitors passing through to Matlock Bath, had the road diverted through a barrier of solid rock at Scarthin, hence the name "Scarthin Nick". Bridge House, standing at the junction of the roads, north-east of Cromford Bridge, was once the home of the Crompton-Evans family, the founders of modern British banking. With the exception of Bridge House, Sir Richard Arkwright had the whole of Willersley razed to the ground. New properties were erected at Cromford for mill workers and Willersley as a village disappeared. Like many other wealthy gentlemen of the period Sir Richard found time to speculate in the lead mines. Gradually he enclosed waste land, took over mines and his son Richard eventually became a lessee of the duty of lot and cope of lead, and held the office of Barmaster in the Wapentake of Wirksworth under the Duchy of Lancaster from 1811. Sir Richard also had upwards of 50,000 trees planted annually on the slopes which had been denuded by lead miners in search of timber, and for firing their smelting "boles".

Retracing one's steps to Scarthin Nick (296.570) either by Mill Lane, or by the footpath behind the Church along the river bank (occupying the site of the pre-1790 road), continue towards Matlock, and after some 300 yards Arkwright's Masson Mills are on the right. The earliest part of the Mill was erected in 1783, and powered by water from the river and partly pumped by a wheel from the Hagg Mine level east of the Derwent. On the 24th December 1772 the subject of a grant to George White and Robert Shore by the Lords of the Manor, empowered them to convey water to their paper mills for 21 years. The paper mill had its foundations adjacent to the first mill at Masson and it seems evident that, with the passage of time, it was acquired by Arkwright. According to a paper published in 1811 by the Rev. Davies, forty people were employed in the manufacture of brown, blue and writing paper. Old ropes cut into small pieces, untwisted and ground-up were used to manufacture brown paper, whilst coarse cotton and white rags were used for the blue and writing paper. It was pressed, separated, sized and dried, then packed so rapidly that two men could make ten reams per day. Weir No. 7 had been in existence long before Arkwright came on the scene. It was small, designed to power

93

a water-wheel and like the other six upstream, was used to unwater lead mines below the level of the river.

The Matlock gorge widens at this point and in the dry season the river bed is often exposed, so here was a place that was able to accommodate a timber aqueduct to the paper mill, later a weir was thrown across the river, then with the erection of the cotton mill a weir of much greater proportions was constructed a little to the south of the earlier one. The mill manager's house on the south side of the premises was occupied for a time by Mr. Need, who had been one of the original partners at Cromford. Subsequently a Chapel was added and endowed by Lady Glenorchy, wife of a Scottish Laird of MacGregor, in gratitude for her escape from injury when the wheel of her carriage broke at this place during a journey to London. In 1831 the Minister here was the Rev. T. M. Newnes, father of George Newnes, founder of the publishing firm. With other local dignitaries Sir George Newnes later caused a Cable Railway, based on those at San Francisco, to be built up Matlock Bank. It ran from 1893 until scrapped in 1927. The mill manager's house and Glenorchy Chapel were demolished in 1956, preparatory to the widening of the road and Scarthin Nick in 1960.

High on the opposite side of the road to Masson Mill, stands Masson House (293.573), once the home of Adam Woolley, who in 1837, bequeathed to the British Museum more than 50 large bound volumes of manuscripts relating mainly to Derbyshire history. They form one of the most important records of early lead mining in existence. Below Masson House, the recent road widening scheme, one of many over the centuries, has completely opened up the gorge between Wildcat Tor, across the river, and Harp Edge, altering the character of this area out of all recognition. The west side of the A.6 road has been hewn out and new limestone walls built to retain the face of solid rock. Here, opposite the mill of 1783, a terrace of brick three storey dwellings has been demolished; they were built originally to house the orphans put to work fourteen hours a day, six days a week, in the cotton mill. Later, dwellings of gritstone had been built alongside and 50 yards to the south, a public house the Rutland Arms and six other similar cottages together with a shop were all demolished between 1970-73.

Opposite the Mill Chimney the recent improvements have obliterated Holland Mine, situated in the kitchen garden of New Masson House with its entrance at the roadside. A hundred yards up the valley stood Warm Walls Gate with its adjoining toll house removed thirty years ago when improvements were made at Weirside. Gone also another three storey Georgian residence, once the "Kings Head", later occupied by a manager at the mill. Immediately on the left, the old bridle road to Upperwood, known as the Wapping is still available to travellers on foot though the steep cobbled entrance passing the front door of the Kings Head has disappeared for ever. This was once the only route to Matlock through the Dale. From Upperwood the path went downhill through Brinswood, near the site of Holme Road then fording the river near Matlock Bath Station, to Mettesford, via Side Lane to Starkholmes and Matlock Town. The coach road to Matlock from the south was Willersley Lane from Cromford Bridge and this was the only road to Matlock that has never been controlled by a turnpike trust. (i.e. no toll bar).

At Warm Walls Gate the road over the Bath Terrace, a tufa bank formed by the outfall of thermal springs over thousands of years, leads to the New Bath Hotel, opened in 1883 on the site of a bath house, the second spring to be commercialised in the Dale. The accommodation here was constructed about 1750 on the site of Hascomb Leys Farm. A thermal bath still exists in the basement of the Hotel and the spring discharges into the river at the south end of Derwent Gardens.

Beyond the Parish Church, terraced land on the left, now a car park, is the site of the first warm spring to be utilised. The Old Bath spring had long been used by the Woolleys of Riber, principle owners of the Manor of Matlock, who had cut a bathing place out of the Marl rock called Woolley's Well. In 1696 the original bath was paved and built by the Rev. Joseph Ferne, Rector of Matlock, Benjamin Hayward of Cromford, Adam Woolley of Allen Hill, Matlock and George Wragg of that place at their own expense. It was afterwards put into the hands of Wragg who took a lease of it from the copyholders of the Manor of Matlock for 99 years, paying them £150 and the yearly rent of sixpence each. In 1698 the bath was a large lead-lined box which proved inadequate though Wragg had constructed a few small rooms adjoining, said to have been but a poor convenience to visitors. Wragg sold his lease to Smith and Pennel, of Nottingham for £1,000 and they erected commodious buildings together with stables and other conveniences. They constructed a road to Matlock Bridge followed by that previously mentioned, to the south in 1745. The Royal Hotel was later to grace this site but was destroyed by fire about the end of the Great War. With the construction of the car park the spring was piped underground but it was not diverted and still discharges into the Fish-pond at the Pavilion and from there to the river. A century or so ago the pool of water at this point was used as a carriage wash, as will be seen from the ancient milestone still in its original place where the flow enters the pond. It was then known as the Old Bath horse pond from the fact that adjoining stables could accommodate 48 animals.

This area has a long and varied history of mining believed to go back long before the Romans arrived, many of the old workings are claimed to have been the result of the work of hostages, slaves and prisoners of war, who under their oppressors were compelled to win the ore coveted by their masters. During the wars with France, prisoners were used in the mines, of that there is no doubt, but perhaps our earliest record, the Domesday survey mentions an ancient "Lead Work", which refers to Matlock Bath. With the discovery of thermal springs and their utilisation for medicinal purposes it is interesting to note the efforts to improve the quality of supply and accommodation. The third spring became known as the Fountain Bath, which later became the local swimming bath on North Parade, now an aquarium. The Fountain Bath had been lower in temperature than its predecessors and it was imagined that the spring had mixed with surface water somewhere underground. Several mines were operating in the vicinity and it was decided to drive a level under Guilder Eye in an attempt to divert the cold spring. In the summer of 1786 the work met with success and the warm water was conveyed by stone channel into the bath house. Some twenty years ago it was estimated that the outflow of water here was in the region of 80,000 gallons per hour.

After this diversion take the bridle road from Weirside to Upperwood, via the Wapping where, after a hundred yards, on the left, the woodland containing some foreign trees forms part of the garden of Masson House. Here enclosures once housed examples of local wild-life, including the Golden Eagle. The Woolley family were Lords of the Manor for 500 years. Adam Woolley had been brought up in the legal profession; he had two daughters, one of whom married Charles Clarke, an attorney and they resided here. With the death of Mrs. Clarke the last local link with that family in this area was at an end. Mr. Clarke is said to have been a regular commuter to London when featuring in high court cases. He held office of Barmaster for the Soke and Wapentake of Wirksworth for many years, adjudicating the complicated disputes between miners and landowners and miners and miners but his particular successes are said to have been in connection with disputes concerning tythes.

95

Here in these grounds it is possible to see the entrance to the Wapping Mine, last worked in the 1950s when a miner found a George II shilling washed out by the rainwater, later the same man found an 18th century "work token", in the mine. It was the value of a penny, bearing the head and inscription of "John Wilkinson— Iron Master", and on the reverse, an illustration of the iron forge of Wilkinson's works in Shropshire.

Continuing up the Wapping, the Cumberland Cavern is reached (292.577). Although a show cave since 1780, it had previously been worked for lead as the Duke of Cumberland Mine and connecting passages lead to Wapping Mine. Most of the show cave is natural solution cave, but following much vandalism the entrance level collapsed in 1971 blocking access and causing accumulation of carbon dioxide in places beyond.

The path leads up to the hamlet of Upperwood (291.579), once a thriving mining village. To the right and well below the road, in the top of the woods is the recent opencast working on the site of the **Royal** or Pavilion **Mine**, where fine calcite crystals can be seen in the cliff face. Concealed entrances lead to mine workings ramifying under Upperwood to link with the **Hopping** and **Jacob's Mines**. With their extensive fluorspar deposits these were once partly open as show-places under the name of **Fluorspar Cavern**. The tourist entrance to the latter is now walled up, but one can still imagine the fine lighting effects obtained by discharging a Bengal flare in the mine and seeing the reflections from a myriad of crystals. Over 150 years ago another show cave beneath Upperwood called the New Speedwell level was opened but it was largely destroyed during the Royal Mine workings in the 1950s.

Passing through Upperwood the road passes the former entrance to the Hopping Mine (291.581) on the left, and after some bungalows there is a path up to the former entrance to the **Devonshire Mine** (290.584), another lead mine turned show cave, but now partly collapsed.

The road descends steeply until the West Lodge of the **Heights of Abraham** is reached (292.584). On paying a small fee, admission is gained to the Zig Zag walks through hillside from where at intervals a magnificent view is obtained of the valley to the south, whilst eastwards lies the hamlet of Starkholmes and Riber Castle, then, sweeping round southwards, Willersley Castle is just hidden by the rising cliff that forms a background to the Derwent. Higher up these walks the **Rutland Cavern** (293.586) is well worth a visit, being open to the public throughout the season. First mined by vertical shafts and then called **Nestus Mine**, Rutland Cavern was opened to the public in 1810 and was renamed in honour of the Duke of Rutland. The present adit was driven then through toadstone into underlying limestone beds containing mineral deposits. Apart from the lead ore, there are spectacular convolutions of fluorspar and barytes, and traces of the uncommon mineral rosasite (copper-zinc carbonate) and the rare cinnabar (mercury sulphide). Large bodies of ore have been mined out long ago leaving vast open chambers and documents three centuries old mention a "great open " excavated even earlier.

Beyond the tourist route the mine breaks into uncharted workings in the Great Rake beneath the floor of the Masson Caverns. Branching up from the path in the Rutland Cavern are the Roman Stairs, leading to higher workings. Tradition has it that a Roman sentry stood guard over the slaves here, but there is no real evidence to support such a story. It is not unlikely, however, that this mine was worked in Roman times and the small pick marks could have been made then. More recently, in 1086, the Domesday Book was probably referring to the Nestus (now Rutland) Mine when it listed "one lead work at Mestesford". During 1671 it yielded lead ore worth £2,400. Nestus Mine was extensively worked in the 18th century.

Outside the Rutland Cavern, and close to Tower House are numerous mine shafts, now mostly covered. Some are over 200 feet deep and lead into the lower part of Old Nestus Mine, now inaccessible. A little higher, in a clearing, is the Victoria Tower (293.587), from where really magnificent views are obtained of the whole area of the Matlocks.

The walk so far covered, and indeed that ahead, abounds with the workings of the 'old man', as the lead miner of former times is referred to, but unfortunately many of these old workings are quite unfit for the inexperienced and the dangers cannot be over-emphasised. Interested parties anxious to see mines and mining relics are well advised to seek the co-operation of such an organisation as the Peak District Mines Historical Society. Behind the Victoria Tower, by the footpath from Bonsall to Matlock Dale, and just inside the Heights of Abraham property, is yet another cavern, known as the **Great Masson Cavern** (292.587), usually open for inspection at weekends. The first part of Masson Cavern follows the Great Rake vein, and is narrow between two vertical walls of limestone, but further in it follows part of the ramifications of the great fluorspar pipe-veins, through a series of large, partly natural chambers, many of which show pockets with short pick-marks where early miners, perhaps Roman, hacked out the lead-ore. At present the rear part of the cavern is blocked off but the workings continue northwards through a maze of workings connecting Black Ox, High Loft, Crichman, King Mine, Queen Mine, Knowles Mine and the Masson openworks. The passages in this maze total over 5 miles in length and include several short coffin levels. These mines were very rich following the discovery of Gentlewoman's Pipe (now known as King Mine) during the mid 17th century.

Crichman Pipe and High Loft mines were worked continuously by father and son for almost fifty years. As a mining family the Pearsons can be traced back for several centuries; one had worked the Cumberland Mine, nearly two hundred years ago. The group of mines, Crichman pipe, Black Ox and High Loft, being closely connected, had enabled this family to produce, wash and screen fluorspar underground, the mineral being brought to the surface ready for loading onto vehicles for delivery to customers. Being unaffected by the elements the work could continue throughout the year. In 1971 a road was made to a point about 200 yards down the hillside and an adit was driven to strike the workings of Black Ox and thereby eliminate haulage by way of shafts. Some years after the death of his father, the son sold his interest in the mine and by 1973, work ceased. From at least 1772 until 1854 the mines hereabouts were worked by various members of the Knowles family and they produced much lead, besides supplying fluorspar for use as a smelting flux at the Ecton copper mine in Staffordshire.

Knowles Mine, together with associated workings, operated successfully under another family ownership throughout the 1930s, but by 1939, ownership had passed to a firm that developed from the amalgamation of a number of small family limestone quarries, here in Matlock, about ten years previously. Derbyshire Stone Limited commenced the openwork at the summit of Masson, west of Magpie Wood, during the early years of the last war and with the introduction of Town and Country Planning Regulations, Ministerial approval was granted for this work to continue within a limited area, in May 1951. It was found beneficial to combine the production of limestone, dolomite and fluorspar with associated gangue minerals and transport them downhill to Cawdor Quarry for treatment. A few years after the war circumstances changed, the dolomite of suitable quality was exhausted, the fluorspar became uneconomic and the limestone required too much handling. No doubt the increasing public outcry in respect of the prospect of a changing skyline on Matlock's

97

most prominent hill had some effect on the decision to abandon these workings. By this time Hall-Dale Quarry was in production for limestone and with a cleaner vertical face, plus a comparative short haul to the main crusher was an economical necessity.

The openworks on Masson (284.592) indicate a complicated geological history. A mass of limestone caught between two layers of the volcanic toadstone (note blocks in walls on the summit) was partly converted by the processes of mineral deposition into dolomite. Subsequently part of this was dissolved away and replaced by fluorspar, with limited amounts of galena, and of nodular grey barytes. At some stage underground streams wore out caves which later became filled with the sands and silts from the melting ice in the Great Ice Age. The early miners followed any available weakness in the rock in search of lead ore, riddling the area with numerous workings. A careful traverse of the walls of this open pit and a study of the relation- ship of the various rocks and minerals to each other can be most rewarding and will demonstrate the changing conditions in which the "Old Man" searched for his ore here. After purchasing the minerals several years ago, Laporte Industries Limited reopened this site in 1973. The world-wide demand for fluorspar in recent years has caused many international mining concerns to turn their attention to Derbyshire and boreholes have been put down throughout the mineralised region. To date none seems to have produced sufficient evidence for a major operation. In the case of Masson hill some three months work using caterpillar excavators to remove over- burden has once again proved that modern methods of opencast working to extract fluorspar here is uneconomic and the operation is now reduced to that of sorting through material tipped by the previous company. Unless a revival of underground mining takes place here one can expect cessation of activity in the near future.

From Masson Mine, footpaths can be taken in several directions; to the south through woodland, it is possible to pass many old mine workings en route to Ember Lane and Bonsall; or another path leads back to Upperwood and via Wapping to Cromford; yet another leads to Cromford via Harp Edge, facing down into Via Gellia. Alternatively a return may be made through the grounds to rejoin the road down from Upperwood to Matlock Bath; or to the north a path leads past Cliff House, perched high on the hillside, and down to the north end of the Dale towards Matlock Town. Adjacent to this last path stands High Tor House (295.593), once the property of Admiral Collingwood, who commanded Nelson's flagship at Trafalgar.

From Matlock Bath, a short diversion may be made into High Tor grounds, where on payment of a small fee it is possible to explore the **Fern** and **Roman Caves**. (297.590). These are strictly not caves, but very old mine-workings, largely roofless. The ore and gangue minerals have been almost completely removed from the outcrop of part of the Great Rake and two branch veins, leaving deep narrow defiles, with numerous traces of pick-marks.

An alternative to this short return route into the Dale would be to take the path from Masson Cavern, north-westwards, across the hillside to reach Salters Lane, so called from the fact that salt was once carried from Cheshire to Chesterfield along this route. The summit area is scarred by removal of limestone and minerals, however one can reach it without great difficulty although fences must be followed for some distance to find a stile. Beware of many old mine shafts, e.g. King and Queen Mines. The best access is by way of Salters Lane, turning west in the direction of Bonsall, where on reaching the summit of the hill a lane leads off to the left into the fluorspar workings.

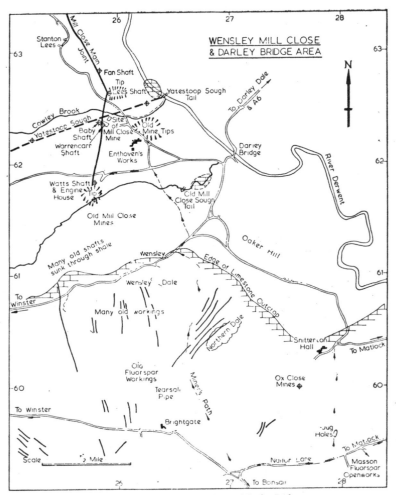

A sketch map of the Wensley, Mill Close and Darley Bridge area.

A return to Matlock may be made down Salters Lane, or the walk may be continued by turning in the opposite direction towards Bonsall. Two routes may be taken by one of two footpaths on the right. The first is soon reached and a path leads through Jug Hole Wood, past the large open entrance to Jug Holes (279.595), part cave and part mine, and so down into Snitterton over intensively worked ground. From Snitterton a return may be made to Matlock or the road past Oaker Hill may be taken to join the main road from Darley Dale to Wensley and Winster at Cross Green, just above the Parish Church. Almost opposite, across the road, the stile admits one to the footpath across the "Clouds", a local term. to reach the site of Mill Close Mine, described later.

99

The alternative route is to continue past the path to Jugholes until another path is reached near the junction of Salters Lane with the Bonsall to Winster road. Here, the roads actually form a triangle but that on the right hand has become disused by vehicles and overgrown. A few yards along, the stile will be seen on the right (271.593) and this, the "Miners' Path", leads across the rim of Masson, below Brightgate, descending into Wensley Dale, then climbing a short distance to reach the village square, from where it is possible to visit the site of Mill Close Mine.

The Miners' Path, a well known local term some thirty or more years ago, was the way used by the miners of Wirksworth, Middleton and Bonsall to reach Mill Close. Being employed on shift working they came over the hills by day and night, their way illuminated by the miners' lamps they carried, and the people of Wensley could set their clocks by the tiny flickering lights of groups of two or three gradually getting nearer. There was hardly a family within ten miles of the mine who at one time did not have a member or relative employed there.

Mill Close Mine: From the village square, the road downhill to Cross Green and Darley Bridge passes Wensley Hall. Some 200 yards further downhill, a stile by a field on the left, known locally as "the Clouds", leads to a footpath across the fields, towards the road from Darley Bridge to Mill Close. About 100 yards downstream from the footbridge on this path is the tail to Old Mill Close sough (265.618).

At the road turn to the left, uphill for a short distance, past old mine tips on the right, and a view is obtained across the valley of Darley, with the lead-smelting works of H. J. Enthoven and Sons Ltd., in the immediate foreground. These works occupy the site of the Mill Close Mine, enabling one to gain some impression of the extent of this former Mine property, for here until 1939 was one of the world's most productive Lead Mines, with a recorded production of nearly half a million tons of lead ore.

Continuing uphill, the road becomes a track and enters Clough Wood, but by bearing a little to the left (the track to the right leads to Birchover) and then straight on, a clearing reveals a valley on the left hand with a stream and the remains of mine tips that have been reworked for their mineral content in recent times. The way ahead is over mine tips for another 50 yards, along the hillside to the remains of old buildings. This was the site of the **Old Mill Close Mine** generally known as 'Watts Shaft' (258.618). Water was pumped by an engine situated in this building, and the large opening was not a window, but designed to allow the 'Beam' to move up and down activating the Pump Rods in the Shaft, each rhythmic movement drawing water from a sump at shaft bottom to the level of the Sough.

The tail to **Yatestoop Sough** may be seen by returning to the road past Enthoven's Works, and turning northwards towards Stanton. Immediately after the tips on the right the road crosses Cowley Brook. If this is followed downstream by the track on the north bank as far as the Derwent, a few yards to the north the tail will be found in a recess in the river bank (263.626). Watts Engine House and the nearby tips are virtually all that can now be seen of the fabulous Mill Close Mine, a sorry record to the vast amount of energy expended there. Whilst on this spot, however, it is worth stopping to think of the fluctuating fortunes of the companies concerned, and on the difficulties and set-backs they overcame.

In 1720, the London Lead Company, often referred to as the 'Quaker Company', heard of the lead miners in Derbyshire and after enquiries, sent two of their members from the lead mines in Flint, to this part of Derbyshire. Their visit brought the Company to decide on taking several leases and on the 13th September in that year, George Greaves, brother of the Mine Agent to the Duke of Rutland, was instructed, acting through his brother and with his advice, to take up a lease of 100 meers of ground, along old disused veins which had been proved good by previous workings, but were at that time waterlogged and to register these in the Barmaster's Book, paying twelve pence per meer for each registration. These mines were situated in Bank Pasture, Winster Liberty.

A meer, measured along the length of the vein, in this part of Derbyshire is 32 yards in length and includes the use of a ground each side of the vein 7 to 8 yards wide to provide room on which to deposit spoil and erect buildings called 'Coes' and other mining facilities. The shafts, mostly flooded, had an average depth of 30 fathoms. In 1723 there were ten veins producing ore and by the close of that year a sough to unwater them had been driven 100 fathoms. Mining had probably been going on here for centuries beforehand. The veins outcrop on the limestone slopes around Wensley village and it was only natural that they should be followed down slope beneath the progressively increasing cover of shales, with attendant increased drainage problems.

In 1741, the London Lead Company decided to purchase old workings on Mill Close Vein in Wensley Liberty to the east of Bank Pasture, for £1,050.

In 1742 a sough reached Mill Close vein to the south of Clough Wood Valley. At this period a stream was diverted to operate a water wheel underground for the purpose of pumping water out of the workings. On 12th December 1751, they started driving Cowley or Yatestoop Sough from Cowley Brook and it is said to have taken the next twenty-one years to reach its objective costing £30,000. It drained the mines in the Winster-Birchover region and was later extended to the mines at Elton. At the same time (1743), Mill Close Sough was also being driven westward through Mill Close Vein and associated workings.

The water-wheel was not a success; the sough was too shallow at the Mill Close vein intersection and other means of drainage were sought. In August 1748 it was decided to install a Newcomen type pumping engine on the south side of the brook opposite Watts Shaft and on the 30th November a Cylinder of 42 inches diameter was supplied by Abraham Darby of Coalbrookdale. Assembly took place on the site and the 47 horse power engine was put into operation. The Company proceeded with Yatestoop mine and the drainage level carried forward, but it would appear that they realised that by unwatering their own mines they would benefit others and so in 1757 a partnership was formed of all persons who would derive benefit from this level and the enterprise continued as the "Yatestoop and Cowley Sough Partners", therefore the £30,000 cost was not borne solely by the Company. The difficulties were obviously enormous and no doubt strained the financial position of the Company for it appears that they were looking into means of economising and on the 1st May, 1759 a trial run was made with the steam pumping engine for a period of 24 hours. It used 4 tons 11 cwts. of Coal, at a cost of 12/- per ton. On the 15th May, 1759, an agreement was made to sell the engine to Thos. Stephens of Dalefield Mine, but the sale was deferred by mutual agreement, as the engine would have to keep operating until completion of the sough or they would not derive any benefit.

In September, 1764, five years later, a Company minute reads, "Mill Close Mine, Derbyshire, has been effectively tried under level and there is no prospect of success. Resolved to stop the Fire Engine and sell the Coal and store such material as will not spoil".

Mill Close ceased work, except perhaps for a skeleton staff, and there was very little, if any, mining after 1764. The Sough was completed and the engine was sold to the Gregory Mine at Ashover, where it worked until 1803.

The London Lead Company took over further mines near the head of Mill Close level in the year 1766, making a very compact holding in that area.

One of their greatest difficulties was transport; the ore had been sold to local smelters or transported to their own works in Flint until 1734, when the Company decided to smelt locally and leased Bowers Smelt Mill at Ashover for 21 years. The lease was renewed in 1755 for 15 years and again in 1770 for a further 21 years the lease being finally surrendered in 1778.

Between 1735 and 1737 the existing furnaces were taken out and new ones erected to the London Lead Company's own design. Local masons were employed, but each had to enter into a bond of £100 "not to build or erect a like furnace or furnaces for the space or term of twenty-one years next ensuing, or for the use or benefit of any other person".

In 1771, along with other proprietors of the district, the London Lead Company obtained an estimate from Brindley for the cost of making a Canal from Chesterfield to Stockwith, on the Trent, a project that had already been surveyed in 1769, the total length of the proposed 'cut' being 44 miles, 6 furlongs. It is on record that the Company subscribed liberally to this project and that they had already shared the cost of the Chesterfield to Ashover Turnpike, so that with improved roadways and a Canal the problem of getting their smelted lead to the Hull market would be eased considerably. Yet a decision like this is remarkable taking into account the fact that in that year 1771, an estimate was made of the cost of unwatering Mill Close preparatory to the re-opening of the mine and then considered to be too high, although it will be remembered that the company had other works within the Mill Close holding.

At this period the Company's interests in the North of England were flourishing and no further leases were taken or renewed in any other area except Cumberland and Durham. The Derbyshire accounts for the year 1775 showed a loss and in 1776 a special meeting was held to consider the Derbyshire undertakings.

A half share in the Yatestoop and Cowley Sough was sold for £2,640 to the other partners and all the mines in Derbyshire except Mill Close, Watering Close and Ballington Wood were sold and these three mines were only maintained in a small way. Several 'Takers' mines and the Smelt Mill were sub-let and in 1778 activity by the Company in Derbyshire ceased, but it was not until 1792 that the London Lead Company surrendered all leases.

For almost a hundred years Mill Close stood idle until in 1859, Mr. Wass reopened the mine and erected Watts in 1860. It was a 50 inches diameter cylinder, Cornish engine made by Thornewill and Warham of Burton-on-Trent. Watts shaft was deepened a further 20 fathoms and this engine worked until 1874.

In 1861, ore began to be raised and continued without interruption for the next fourteen years. Warren Carr shaft was sunk to 50 fathoms in 1874 and a 60 inches diameter cylinder Cornish engine named "Jumbo" was erected. This engine had a 10 feet stroke and made seven strokes per minute. The following year (1875) Warren Carr was drowned, interrupting production until 1877. In the year 1881, Lees shaft was sunk; it was deepened to 73 fathoms in 1901 and a steam winder was used until 1939, with the chimney stack still standing.

On the death of Mr. Wass in 1886 the mine came under the control of his trustees until 1919.

A new engine house was built alongside the earlier one at Warren Carr in 1889, to house two Cornish engines. One was the 1859, 40 inches diameter cylinder, with a stroke of 10 feet, named "Baby", the other a 50 inches diameter cylinder engine brought from Wakebridge Mine, near Crich, named "Alice". These two engines pumped water up an oval section shaft, from a depth of 50 fathoms and the old Mill Close shaft now became known as "Harvey's engine shaft". "Jumbo", "Baby", and "Alice" all discharged the water drawn by them into the old Yatestoop sough at a point some 60 feet below surface and via the sough tail it entered the river Derwent.

The Warren Carr shaft was deepened another 20 fathoms soon after the turn of the century at which time it was 70 fathoms deep. A small electric pump was installed to lift water to the 50 fathom level, where it could be drawn up by "Baby" and "Alice" when "Jumbo" had to stop for any reason. Perhaps here we have a hint of "Jumbo" nearing the end of his usefulness and a new source of power being gradually introduced. There were extensions made to one engine house in 1911, but to which one is not clear. A fire in 1920 burned the grease-soaked beams of "Jumbo" house and repairs were effected using steel joists.

By 1922 a new company was formed, known as the Mill Close Mines Ltd. acquiring the property on the recommendation of the late Dr. Malcolm Maclaren. Technical control lay with the New Consolidated Gold Fields Ltd. and with the new owners came modernisation. "Jumbo" was scrapped in 1931; an electric winder was installed and this shaft became the main mineral hoist. Two stand-by diesels had to be installed because the pumps were drowned if stopped for more than 2 hours. Water and the constant threat of flooding had always been a menace at Mill Close, and as the workings extended the problem grew. In 1887 the quantity of water pumped from the workings was 1,000 gallons per minute, by 1920 it had increased to 1,600 gallons per minute; 1929, 2,000 gallons; 1937, 4,300; in 1938 a further increase brought the amount to 5,550 gallons per minute. The Pilhough fault encountered in February, 1938, driving west on the 144 fathom level, brought a permanent increase to the inflow of water of 1,000 gallons per minute. The sudden inrush of water rose almost to the 103 fathom level before it could be checked and with all the available pumps brought into action, night and day, it took over a month to gain control and six months passed by before the workings were clear enough to ascertain that the ore body was lost and no others apparent.

Shortly before this event it had been estimated that the weight of water lifted from the workings to the sough was in the region of 30,000 tons per day. The early 1930's had been a difficult period with the price of lead sometimes below £10 per ton, but it was estimated that 10,000 tons of crude ore had been mined per month. About this period a production record of 800 tons of crude ore and 7 million gallons of water were brought to the surface from 900 feet below ground in a day. The maximum depth of workings was 170 fathoms and the mineral deposit worked extended towards Rowsley. During this period the mine and adjoining smelter employed over 700 men.

During the latter years the old mine tips on the property were systematically re-dressed by passing the tailings through the modern methods of "Froth-flotation". Very finely ground lead and zinc ores were extracted which had previously been lost to the tailings dam. In dressing ore the miners of former times had washed and jigged the crude material, the dirty water being passed into a dam carrying with it material in suspension. This settled overnight from each days work and the clear water was either used again or allowed to drain off, but this soon built up into a large tip, the sides of which would have to be strengthened by adding a more solid material and often the centre region of the dam would be pumped out or taken out by hand (when solid enough) and deposited around the perimeter where it would dry out in favourable weather. This method has long been common practice, the author himself having made dams in this way, using the slimes, but only by experience is it possible to determine what pressure the wall of the dam will stand according to the material flowing into it. Although having a crust at surface it will always be soft beneath and remain slime. Dams deposited well over a hundred years ago have recently been found to be extremely 'slimy' near the centre, although the surface has held vehicles passing over them.

The large tailings dam north of Enthoven's works remained untouched for thirty years except for small areas on the perimeter containing quarter inch chippings, mostly a mixture of calcite, limestone and about 15% fluorspar, used locally for road grit in winter, as gravel for garden paths and in the manufacture of floor tiles.

Although much of the lead-zinc content had been reclaimed during the final years of Mill Close Mine, chemical depressants used in froth-flotation included Sodium Cyanide, Crysilic Acid, Caustic Soda, Xanthate, Copper Sulphate, Paraffin, Pine oil, etc; so it was not long before local poultry-keepers found that the use of this material in their gardens had disadvantages.

The introduction of more efficient treatment plant at the Hopton works of Messrs. C. E. Giulini Limited, has enabled vast quantities of hitherto unsuitable low grade materials to be brought in from surrounding areas to be re-treated, and since 1971 the Mill Close tips have been considerably reduced by modern rapid loading and haulage methods in order to provide immense quantities of mineral required to keep this plant in full-time operation. The former tailings dam in Cawdor Quarry, all that now remains of the Megdale mineral dressing plant, is at present being transported in large lorries to Hopton works for re-treatment. Such examples serve to illustrate how eyesores of yesterday can be removed and put to profitable purpose whilst at the same time reclaiming areas of derelict land, though unfortunately there is still a waste disposal problem.

The years 1938-39, saw the closure of the mine with the inevitable removal of engines, winding gear and dressing plant, sold to mining concerns in other areas or for scrap according to its value. The site with remaining buildings and smelter was taken over by H. J. Enthoven and Sons Ltd. and the smelting of lead, chiefly from scrap material, has continued to the present time. "Jumbo" engine house was demolished in 1966, and replaced by a large asbestos shed though part of the earlier engine house is still standing. At Lees shaft only the gritstone chimney remains as evidence of the site of the former mine yard engine house and winding gear, the property now occupied by new buildings for the manufacture of concrete products.

The whole of the galena output at Mill Close Mine from the time when Mr. Wass began to raise ore in 1861 until closure of the mine in 1939 amounted to 430,000 tons of concentrate averaging over 81% Lead. At present day prices this would be worth close on £25 million. The fluorspar now being recovered may well be worth more than £5 million.

The workings extended for over a mile to the north, in the limestones beneath the shale and Millstone Grit cover, at times to a depth of 1,000 feet below the level of the river. No wonder the pumping engines had difficulty in keeping up with the inflow, as they were trying to cope with the rainfall on several square miles, as well as streams such as the Lathkill leaking into their own beds, and thus via the veins of the Alport Mines to Mill Close Mine.

From Wensley buses run to Matlock, with connections to Cromford, Bakewell, etc.

10. The Crich Area

2½ inches: 1 mile, Map SK 35; 6 inches: 1 mile, Maps SK 35 NW & SW.

Geologically, the Crich area forms in miniature an equivalent of the whole of Derbyshire. It is an upfolded mass of limestone a mile long and ¼ mile wide, surrounded by Millstone Grits and shales, riddled with numerous mineral veins, particularly in the area around Wakebridge and Crich Cliff. The natural resources of the Crich area have been exploited over many centuries. The area has been extensively mined over a long period for lead but in the second half of the 19th century a decline in the price of lead forced the closure of many mines. Since that time the growing, importance of the minerals which occur with the lead has induced periods of revival in mining activity, with lead being a by-product. Extensive quarries in the area are evidence of the quest for limestone used for lime burning and roadstone.

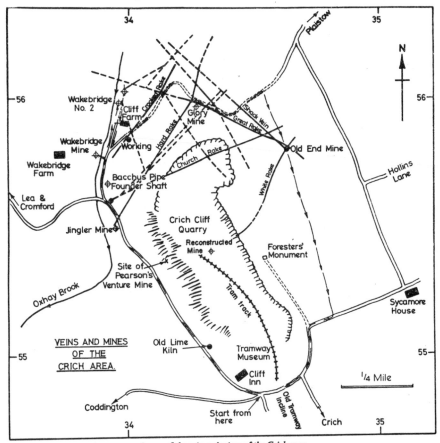

A map of the vein and mines of the Crich area.

105

The limestone mass has been heavily mineralised with veins criss-crossing one another in a general north-west to south-east and north-east to south-west direction. A number of these veins run closely parallel to one another and may be considered to be double veins with a rider of limestone separating them. They have been given names by the old miners such as Merry Bird, Wanton Legs, Strawberry, Silver Eye and Pig Trough.

Rocks of volcanic origin called "toadstone" occur in the limestone sequence varying from a few inches to tens of feet thick, and these affect the mineral content of the veins, as well as under ground drainage. The minerals occurring in the veins are galena, fluorspar, barytes and calcite. Specimens of all these minerals can be found easily on the old mine hillocks.

The best examples of the evidence of mining in the district are to be found in a relatively small area to the north-west of Crich, surrounding the Cliff Quarry, part of which now houses the Tramway Museum.

Commencing at the Cliff Inn (344.548) proceed along the road in the direction of Holloway. On the right of this road the remains of an old lime kiln and evidence of landslipping can be seen. A number of mines have been buried by landslips including Pearson's Venture and Rodney Mines which were engulfed in July 1882 as a result of quarrying operations. At that time the quarry was worked by the Clay Cross Company which had given notice of the possibility of a landslip to the mine owners some two years previously in December 1880. Following one landslip the road itself and a number of cottages were buried.

Approaching Wakebridge a wooden headgear can be seen on the left of the road in a small wooden enclosure. This marks the site of the **Jingler Mine** (340.544). The headgear, erected in the 1920's, forms the main feature of this site. At the time of its erection the workings, mainly for fluorspar, reached a depth of 246 feet, the lower, older workings being under water, though no pumping was necessary at this time. The haulage unit used for winding ore up the shaft had a central winding drum with a cylinder on either side. One cylinder was powered by a coal-fired vertical steam raising boiler and the other cylinder, providing an alternative source of power, utilised compressed air. The ore was dressed on the surface where machinery was installed in buildings constructed of wood and corrugated iron, one of which (the jig shed) was transferred after operations ceased for use at the Golconda Mine, Brassington.

The headgear, believed to be the last remaining of its type connected with lead mining in Derbyshire and preserved by the Peak District Mines Historical Society, was erected over a shaft dating back to the early 19th century. There is evidence that a number of coes constructed of stone (where the miners changed their working clothes) existed on this site during that period. The foundations of one such building may be seen alongside the boundary wall with the road.

This shaft was formerly called Rolley and the name Jingler (or Gingler) first appeared about 1850. There appears to be some confusion between the names given to this shaft and another shaft, sometimes referred to as **Lee's** Shaft, located behind the houses on the opposite side of the road. The workings here were drained by the Ridgeway Sough (also known as the Wakebridge or Whatstandwell Level), which branched beneath nearby Lomas Close, one branch going north to Wakebridge Mine, the other south-east to the Cliff Side Mines, including Pearson's Venture Mine. The water from the Cliff Side Mines was said to be lukewarm.

At one time an underground pumping engine was installed here, coal for which was taken up the sough by boat from its entrance on the River Derwent, near Whatstandwell.

The sough was being driven in 1811 when Farey noted it as the Wakebridge Sough. At that time it was two-thirds of a mile long and was being driven in shale and limestone towards the Cliff Side Mines. A plan of 1829 shows a branch from the south at Lomas Close through Rolley Shaft to the Wakebridge Mine. By the 1850's it was referred to as the Ridgeway Sough and it is this name that appears in the Memoirs of the Geological Survey. In 1880 Stokes referred to it by the earlier name of Wakebridge Sough and stated that it was one mile long.

This sough was unusual in that it was a "standing level" where water was kept at a depth of at least 15 inches to accommodate the boats. The level of the water was maintained by a series of simple locks similar to those known from other lead mine soughs; the water was raised by slotting wooden boards across the sough between stones in the side walls. The level was approximately 4 ft. 6 ins. high and had its tail a short distance from the River Derwent, near Whatstandwell Bridge, between the river and the Cromford Canal below the saw mill. The entrance to the sough was bricked up some years ago and water now issues from a metal pipe on the river bank.

Returning to the road, a trackway shortly joins it on the right. Proceed up this trackway noticing on the right an old hillock, built around a shaft, the Bacchus Founder Shaft, which was used as a climbing shaft. The miners entered this shaft by means of a covered passage from a coe which stood nearby and descended the shaft by a series of ladders into the workings below. The Bacchus Pipe connected with the Wakebridge Mine a short distance away and was used as an access route for this mine in the early 1870s. Over a mile of levels are still accessible.

Continuing along the trackway the ruins of the Wakebridge Mine buildings can be seen on the left (339.557). Here, more complete remains of mining activity than perhaps found elsewhere in the area, are to be seen. These consist of an engine house with its adjacent shaft (walled round), a water storage pond now filled with rushes, and a workshop building, now used for farm storage.

During the late summer of 1967 a large shaft approximately 10 ft. by 12 ft. was uncovered between one of the walled shafts adjoining the engine house and the brook; the purpose of this shaft is as yet unknown and its identification on old plans of the site has not been found to date.

Mining has been carried out on this site since the early 19th century and possibly earlier. The present engine house, originally constructed of stone, was erected on the site of an earlier building which may have had a thatched roof, as was common at many mines of the period. A circular "engine race" shown on a plan of 1829 indicates that ore was raised by a horse-gin at that time.

A steam engine was installed in 1857. Built by Messrs. Thornewill and Warham of Burton-on-Trent, it had a cylinder diameter of 60 inches and a stroke of 8 feet indoors and 7 feet 6 inches outdoors. The engine is said to have been moved to Millclose Mine, Darley Dale, in 1889, though the mine was still in operation at this time and it may have been moved a little later than that. At Millclose it was nicknamed "Alice" and was used as auxiliary engine at this mine until the 1920's.

At Wakebridge the steam engine was used for pumping water to the level of the sough (the Ridgeway Sough) 420 ft. from the surface and raising ore to the surface where it was dressed, sorted and washed.

In February 1863 a breakage in the pumping machinery caused flooding; tools and ore were drowned and work in the lower levels was suspended for a time causing great distress to the miners.

The engine shaft, approximately 650 feet deep, was originally sunk on a pipe vein running north, approximately along the line of the brook. During the late 1880's the miners were working a vein approximately 800 yards north-north-east of the shaft. At that time narrow rails carrying small waggons pushed along by youths, brought the ore from the forefield to the shaft bottom; illumination in the mine was by candlelight. The lower levels had been abandoned at this time owing to faulty machinery and the expense involved, the price of lead being too low to warrant the expense.

The mine has been worked intermittently this century mainly for fluorspar, with some barytes, calcite and lead being obtained. During the period 1921-31 between 5 and 18 men were employed, not more than nine underground and more usually five. During the last period of working from 1945 to the early 1950's no more than five men were employed at one time. Mining operations during this period were undertaken from Wakebridge No. 2 Shaft situated alongside the brook beyond Cliff Farm.

At the time when the Engine House was built in the mid 19th century up to 42 miners were employed. The men were paid 2s. 6d. per day for an 8 hour shift. The Agent of the Mine, James Elce, received £55 per annum. The mine was sufficiently large to employ such tradesmen as carpenters and a blacksmith.

Returning to the old trackway and proceeding towards Cliff Farm, the remains of a series of dams can be seen on the left along the course of the brook. The water from these dams was used for washing the ore at the mine and was piped to the Jingler Mine when it was working during the 1920's.

A short distance along the footpath is the site of Wakebridge No. 2 shaft, now concreted over. It was from here that operations were undertaken during the last period of working when considerable quantities of fluorspar were obtained from old workings. Two levels were worked, one at 168 feet and a lower one at 246 feet. In 1952 the miners were working near a point where the west-north-westerly trending Great Vein reaches the western margin of the limestone inlier; the Hazlehurst Vein which intersects the same ground was also worked. The shaft was equipped for skip hoisting with an electric hoist and diesel driven compressor.

Retracing the route to where the old trackway forks, ascend the hill, passing a present-day working for fluorspar with its attendant machinery on the right.

Evidence of veins, partly filled with debris, can be seen on the hillside. Circling an old shaft hollow the path passes alongside a mining venture commenced in 1967 and worked intermittently since then by an incline driven into the Glory Vein. The corrugated iron buildings from which a mine headgear protrudes near the top of the hill, mark the site of the **Glory Mine** (343.559), which has been worked intermittently for at least 150 years; firstly for lead and later for fluorspar. Good examples of banded vein materials can be obtained along this part of the route.

The mine is said to have been very remunerative, the lowest workings being at a depth of 810 feet. The toadstone which was encountered at a depth of 180 feet was found to be approximately 60 feet thick. In common with other veins in the area they were said to be less productive at depth. In the mid 19th century the shaft was 480 feet deep with six or eight waggon ways.

As with most mines in Derbyshire, disputes often figure in the records. Luke Allsop, the Barmaster in the second half of the 19th century records in his diary for May 7th 1870 that a riot occurred between two factions of dissatisfied miners over the working of Glory Mine and that they had damaged much property; he imposed fines on each miner of 3s. 4d. which they duly paid. Six months previously he had imposed a fine of £3 9s. 0d. on a miner after finding him guilty of practically cutting through the winding rope thereby endangering life.

The corrugated iron buildings and headgear have survived from the period of working in the 1950s and are still in intermittent use.

Rounding the hill a good view can be obtained across the Derbyshire Coalfield. In the near distance the ruins of the engine house at the Old End Mine on the Great Rake can be seen (346.558). This was built on the Cornish principle probably in the mid 19th century. The ruins of the engine house dominate the site which is now covered with grassed over spoil heaps, remaining from the last period of mining activity in the 1940's. Several other veins on the eastern side of the limestone inlier were also worked from this mine.

The main shaft reached a depth of 912 feet and was one of the deepest shafts in Derbyshire and the deepest shaft sunk entirely in limestone. The mine is drained by the Crich Sough (or Fritchley Level) which enters the shaft at approximately 420 feet from the surface. It drains into a brook at Fritchley two miles south-south-east and the arch at its outflow bears the date of 1753. It was driven to unwater a mining title called Hollins Sough Lead Mines in the Parish and Manor of Crich.

An undated plan, possibly of the 1840's, indicates the size of the mining operations at that time for surface buildings, in addition to the engine house, including a whimsey (or winding engine), an ore house, a blacksmith's shop, a reckoning house, and a store shed, of which little evidence now remains.

Mining is said to have ceased in 1864 due to diminishing output and the poorness of veins at depth and the mining plant was offered for sale. The Barmaster, however, recorded in his diary for May 1867 that the company owning the Old End Mine had decided to erect machinery for clearing water out of the lower levels which had been abandoned for some time owing to litigation over disputes arising amongst the shareholders, which had been settled out of Court. Work at the mine proceeded and in 1873 the discovery of a huge cavern is recorded. In September 1879 the owners decided to start to withdraw the pumping gear and prepared to abandon the mine owing to rising costs and the refusal of the Wakebridge Mine owners to pay their agreed share of the expenses. Less than a month later the miners at the Glory Mine, ¼ mile away, found the lower level of the mine flooded due to the withdrawal of pumping machinery at the Old End Mine. The lower levels of the Wakebridge Mine were abandoned six months later in May 1880. The decline in the price of lead and the rising costs were taking their toll of the industry.

In 1908 Drabble Brothers of Matlock took possession of the Mineral Title of Old End Mine with all veins, meers of ground and rights and privileges belonging thereto as well as the Glory Mine and other mines on Crich Cliff. A period of revival of mining activity ensued for a few years.

The last period of mining activity took place in the 1940's when fluorspar was being sought. At that time the main shaft was re-opened to a depth of 300 ft. but the workings were found to be in a poor condition. The shaft has since been filled with debris and only a deep hollow now remains. Open cuts and shallow shafts on

Church Rake and the eastern part of Great Rake were made at that time. Good coarse-grained fluorspar was obtained from a shaft on Greak Rake, 125 ft. deep, approximately 175 ft. west-north-west of the main Old End shaft.

From the Old End Mine follow the footpath to Crich passing below the monument to the Sherwood Foresters to be seen at the crest of the hill on the right. On reaching the road turn right and return to the Cliff Inn. Near the entrance to the Tramway Museum, the old mineral railway from the quarry to Ambergate and the Cromford Canal used to pass under the road. At the further end of the tram track a typical lead mine site has been constructed from materials salvaged from various sites in Derbyshire. A shaft-top with stows, an adit mouth, a miners' coe and crushing circle are to be seen.

11. Carsington Pastures, Brassington

2½ inches: 1 mile, Map SK 25; 6 inches: 1 mile Maps SK 25 SW & SE.
Walking distance—5 miles.

THE MINES ON THE PASTURES :
An undulating grassy upland marks the southern boundary of the Derbyshire lead mining field. Somehow it has partly escaped the Enclosure Acts and is largely devoid of stone wall, and for this reason it has retained the name of Carsington Pastures. Though only 2½ miles from the mining centre of Wirksworth little is known of the detailed history of the ramification of workings and veins. The walk described below can thus only give a limited view of the intense activity which has taken place here in the past. The route is roughly in the form of a square with sides a mile long, bounded by the villages of Brassington and Carsington on the south, and by the minor road between Wirksworth and Brassington on the north. Last worked on any scale were the Nickalum and Great Rake Mines, both producing barytes in 1919. The nearby Condway Mine was worked as recently as 1940-43 and the Golconda Mine finally ceased work in 1953 after over two centuries of intermittent activity. Though the recent working was for barytes, all had been important lead producers earlier. Many of the older workings still have ruined coes where the miners changed their clothes, and there are numerous open shafts.

There are also two small caves; one in Harborough Rocks yielded relics of the Roman occupation of Britain to archeologists some 60 years ago, whilst the other, on Carsington Pasture, shows obvious signs of more recent occupation as a dwelling place, perhaps by Defoe's miner's wife. Shortly before his death in 1731, Daniel Defoe, better known for his "Robinson Crusoe", toured Britain with some friends and visited the Wirksworth area, whence he rode out to see the lead mines and: "We were agreeably surprised to see a hand, and then an arm, and quickly after a head, thrust up out of the very groove we were looking at . . . this subterranean creature . . . was a most uncouth spectacle, clothed all in leather . . . for his person he was lean as a skeleton, pale as a dead corpse, his hair and beard a deep black, his flesh lank, and as we thought something of the colour of the lead itself". Defoe also described visiting a miner's wife and five children who lived happily in "a natural opening in the rock, wherein her husband had been born. The chamber within was divided by a curtain, had shelves with earthenware, pewter and brass. A hole in the roof served as a chimney, and she had a few pigs and a cow enclosed outside . . . She earned, when she could, a few pence per day, washing ore". The cave wherein this mining family resided has usually been taken to be Harborough Cave, which is so much better known, but if the cave on Carsington Pasture is examined with Defoe's account in mind, it could equally well be the place he visited. The chimney and smoke-blackened roof are still to be seen.

A good starting point for the walk is Brassington (232.544), a typical Derbyshire mining village although now the main occupation is agriculture. The village itself has some very interesting buildings and a fine old church. "Branzincton" was listed in the Domesday Book. It is uncertain when mining was first started in this area, but by 1683 there was enough ore being produced to warrant a Deputy Barmaster in the village.

From Town Street the public footpath to Carsington climbs eastwards across the fields to the western edge of Carsington Pasture. After passing through the last stile onto the open grazing land, turn right along the wall where there is a rewarding view of Brassington Village, the church and the uplands behind.

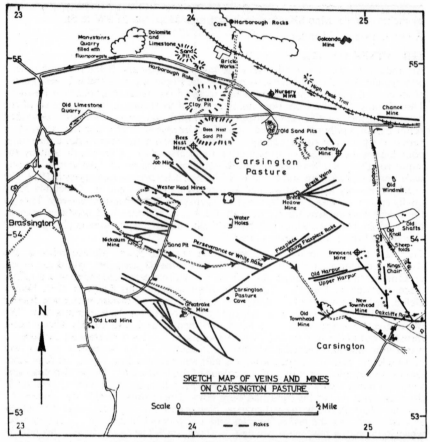

Sketch map of the veins and mines of Carsington Pasture.

Proceeding up the path, just below the crest of the hill two features astride the path may be seen: on the left is an old crushing circle with some track stones still present though the centre stone is missing. Below this to the right of the path is an old settling pond. Where the path begins to level out the gaunt ruins of the **Nickalum Mine** buildings are ahead (237.540). The coe is of comparative recent origin, and beyond this is a building which could have housed an engine, while a concrete cap now covers the main shaft. This shaft is reputed to have "three turns", each of 70 feet, which would give an approximate depth of 200 feet. The Geological Survey Memoirs note the depth as 10 fathoms (60 ft.) but this would not warrant an engine, and may be a misprint. As late as 1919 the Nickalum or Old Brassington Mine was worked for small amounts of caulk, but no galena was being produced.

The mine is said to be in a pipe running west of north, with the strata forming a dome rich in lead, which at one time produced ore to the value of £13,000 in two years. With the exception of the Great Rakes Mine, Nickalum has the only engine house on the Pasture. In 1891 lead was still being produced, a measurement of 35 loads 3 dishes being recorded, but by 1895 no more than five loads were measured for the whole year.

Leaving Nickalum Mine the path curves eastwards and downhill into Wester Hollow a picturesque amphitheatre ringed with limestone outcrops and old lead workings. Descending the path, on the left at the head of the hollow are the Wester Head Mines (239.542) scattered among the rocks at the head of the cart track. Some of these were sunk to a depth of 18 to 30 fathoms in white sand and were worked for cerussite (otherwise known as white lead ore). This is a feature of the area, and such ore has been worked for centuries, sometimes from open sand pits. Occasionally the "old man" following veins in the limestone has come across pockets of sand and white ore underground, but usually the sand, as well as associated fireclays have been dug out from open pits for use in refractory brick making.

To the south across the hollow, is the site of the **Great Rake Mine** (240.536) now only a number of low walls and concrete engine beds. A few years ago the wooden headgear on the main shaft could be seen silhouetted against the sky, but old age and vandals led to its downfall in 1961. The earliest known date for the Great Rake Mine being worked is 1735. The "old man" worked to a depth of 70 fathoms and in 1919 the Geological Survey recorded workings to 50 fathoms, when mostly barytes was being produced, some from a vein varying in width from 4 to 11 feet.

Following the path downhill, some old sand quarries can be seen at the side of the cart track in the bottom of the hollow. On reaching the cart track, go straight across and follow the footpath up the other side of the hollow, and pass slightly to the left of the clump of trees on the skyline. The route now lies through heavily worked country, with innumerable shafts, so care should be exercised and it is advisable to watch where you are putting your feet. A certain eminent geologist exploring an overgrown outcrop for a suspected natural cave, put his foot in a "rabbit hole" and fell headlong down the slope beyond. Investigation showed the "rabbit hole" to be 30 inches in diameter, lined with stone, and about 40 feet deep! Luckily, no injury was sustained. Usually the position of the shafts can be seen from small stone "Beehives" over the top, but occasionally irresponsible persons omit to replace the stones over the top, so a gaping hole is left for the unwary!

Climbing the slope east of Wester Hollow, **Perseverance Rake** or White Rake lies parallel and a few yards to the left. On reaching the brow of the hill, rough worked ground extends in all directions, and the lines of the rakes can be traced by the lines of grass-covered mounds of old spoil heaps along their length. The site of Great Rake Mine presents itself from a different angle half a mile away on the right. Roughly 300 yards east of the ruins a concealed hollow has the hidden entrance to **Carsington Pasture Cave** (241.536). Carsington village can now be seen ahead. As the path descends it crosses the line of White Rake (also known once as Blackbird or Engine Rake) (243.538). This rake runs west to east for approximately 500 yards and according to Farey was being worked for white ore about 1811. The Geological Survey Memoir lists carbonate of lead (cerussite) with an abundance of barytes. There are a number of shafts on this rake and like most others in the area the stonework is still sound, a testimony to some unknown long dead craftsmen!

As the path joins the cart track at the bottom of the slope there are three shafts alongside the track on a line of workings known as Dowsithills. Extending up **the** hillside on the left of the cart track are the twin parallel rakes of Flaxpiece Rake, the Young Flaxpiece worked originally for lead, later for barytes. These rakes are dotted with many shafts and remains of coes, plus some overgrown remains which appear to have been crushing sites, settling dams etc. Barbed wire fences off some of the more dangerous shafts.

Many of the shafts in the area have typical Derbyshire mining names such as Old Horse, Beardsley Founder, Old Harpur, Colt, Appletree Swang, Sing-a-Bed, etc. The cart track is now confined between the steep shoulder of the pastures and a stone wall on the right. Just before the first of two quarries on the left, the twin veins of Old Harpur and Upper extend up the hillside. At the second old quarry (248.536), the workings of the Townhead Mine (1811) cross under the track. The workings of New Townhead (1805-1845) lie under the hillside above the first houses of the village, which comes into sight round the corner. Continuing down the lane past the houses, it joins the road at a right angled bend. If a visit to the church or the Miners' Arms is desired, go straight on down the road.

To continue round the pastures, take the path up a narrow walk between the houses at the point where the lane joins the bend in the road. Reaching the gate at the top of the gardens the path turns right climbing uphill to the top of the wood on the right. A few yards to the left of the path are five shafts on the line of Oakcliffe (= Yokecliffe) Rake, which continues to Nursery End Mine on the right of the path by the stone wall (253.536). The Nursery End Mine was producing calamine (zinc carbonate) and lead prior to 1815. On the left, in line down the hillside are the four shafts of the Cow and Calf workings.

On reaching the corner of the wood, turn sharp left and follow alongside the wall uphill to the King's Chair and Old Knowle Knoll. The King's Chair (253.539) is a crag of dolomite limestone, of which the upper part has been artificially hollowed out into the shape of a throne, probably as a late 18th century pseudo-antiquity or folly. Note the rough nature of the ground on the left, again due to past mining activities, with many shafts still present. The biggest complex of workings bears the name of "Children's Fortune" while further to the left, west of King's Chair is a cluster of shafts of the Innocent Mine (250.538). This mine was working in the late 18th century and Wm. Duesbury of the Crown Derby porcelain works bought an interest in the mine for the "china clay" deposits about 1770 until his partnership lapsed in 1826. The problem of china clay arises at several mines in the area although today geologists say there is no foundation for suspecting that genuine china clay as known today exists in the area. Several pottery manufacturers bought an interest in the mines and exported material to the potteries. The Green Linnets Mine to the west of Brassington was also tried for "china clay" in 1789, but the clay was halloysite, a clay mineral similar to kaolin, with physical properties sufficiently different to make it unsuitable for china-ware. Even so, the late 18th century potters repeatedly used it in experiments. It is associated with the silica sands of the "Pocket Deposits" around Brassington, which are quarried for use in making refractory bricks in the small brickworks by Harborough Rocks.

Passing on, a walled off, heavily overgrown enclosure is seen on the other side of the stone wall on the right. Most likely it was a mine site, for although part of it is noted on the ordnance map as "Sheepfold" there is also a note "Old Shafts". The cartographers of the Ordnance Survey must have become rather tired of writing "Old Shafts" on this particular sheet. No information is available on this site, although at this point a few yards apart on either side of the path are two shafts labelled "Old Knowle" (250.541) on an old map. How old one wonders?

The path continues along the side of the wall to the road, passing on the right the remains of an old windmill in a field. On the left lies the open expanse of the pasture, marred by ugly electricity pylons.

Just before reaching the road the barbed wire fence on the left encloses the **Condway Mine** (248.545) worked to a depth of 140 ft. in the 1940s for barytes from a vein in dolomitized limestone, with many cross joints. Before this the mine was working in 1877 but only 7½ dishes of ore were recorded by the Barmaster.

This was apparently the last of the ore (apart from a small amount of 1879) for in November 1906 the barmaster served notice to work, and in December of that year the mine changed hands. The barmasters' records did not show any ore production from this new management.

Passing the Condway Mine, a metalled road is reached. Cross the road, and two stiles give access to the High Peak Trail on the old Cromford and High Peak Railway line. Here a short diversion to the right (note the old Chance Mine workings on the left) gives a view down the old Hopton Incline, otherwise turn left for Harborough Rocks and Brassington, with the famous **Golconda Mine** buildings coming into view on the right. This mine, one of the most extensive in Derbyshire, has been worked intermittently since at least the 18th century, and possibly earlier, until 1953 and to a depth of 420 ft. There are some 3 miles of galleries on an old mine plan, and the workings encountered several large caverns. On a recent exploration one of these was found to have written in smoke on the wall "I. Rawlinson, 1777", presumably a former miner, but the signatures of "Henry VIII" and "King Tut B.C. 19" were not thought to be genuine! Access to the mine is no longer possible owing to the condition of the winding gear.

Walking along the trail the escarpment of Harborough Rocks is now ahead on the right, whilst on the left the chimney like ruins of Breck Hollow Coe (246.543) can be seen on the pastures. This coe is one of the few still remaining which have the recessed inner corners of the walls said to be built that way to deceive the barmaster on the amount of ore present. The Breck Mine shafts (and there are at least ten) were sunk near the intersection of several veins running north-west and north-east. The early history is obscure, but ore was still being produced in small quantities around 1880. Barytes was also produced at a later date.

Another few minutes walk brings you to the brickworks where a footpath crosses the trail for Harborough Rocks and cave. The climb to the top is well worth the effort, giving an excellent view in all directions, including the former sand pits near the brickworks, now filled with waste slimes from Giulini's fluorspar processing plant at Hopton. Descending from the rocks go straight across the trail, and turn right at the road. Here the road passes close to silica sand workings, of interest to geologists on account of the fossilized *Sequoia* wood in the refractory clays, and to the cover of boulder-clay deposited by the glaciers of the last Ice Age. The silica sands are taken to the brickworks below Harborough Rocks for firing. In a few yards there is a track to a quarry on the left which is still working for sand on the site of the **Bees Nest Mine** the old workings of which have been destroyed during quarrying. There was a shaft 22 fathoms deep and the mine was worked for barytes in 1919. A small amount of ore (1 load 7 dishes) was measured by the barmaster in 1889 but one would expect the mine to be much older than this.

The road now runs alongside Harborough Rake which is marked by occasional old hillocks and shaft mounds. Shortly, the hillside on the left flattens out towards Brassington and from here the road descends quite steeply to a T junction, where a left turn returns to the starting point of the walk in Brassington.

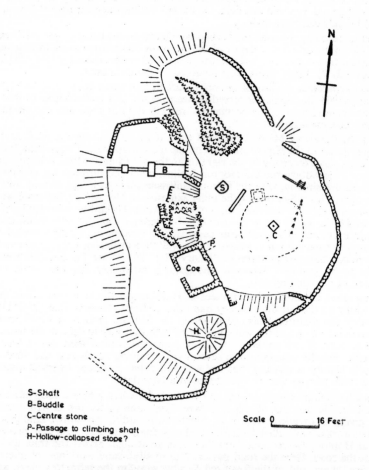

S-Shaft
B-Buddle
C-Centre stone
P-Passage to climbing shaft
H-Hollow-collapsed stope?

Scale 0   16 Feet

Plan of surface remains at Snake Mine, Hopton Wood.

SNAKE MINE, HOPTON WOOD :

After the above walk it may be convenient to visit the surface relics of Snake Mine, Hopton Wood (262.555). Return along the minor road from Brassington towards Wirksworth as far as Hopton cross roads and turn left (north) under the railway. Immediately on the left is the site where Magnesium Elektron Ltd. erected plant to extract magnesium metal from dolomite obtained from an adjacent quarry. This enterprise failed and the buildings have been adopted for fluorspar extraction by a flotation process operated by C. E. Giulini (Derbyshire) Ltd.

About a quarter of a mile to the north, towards Via Gellia, the Hoptonwood Quarry access road is close to the site of Snake Mine. The hillock of this old mine is in the field immediately right (south of the entrance to the quarry road, a few yards south of the sawmill chimney). The artificial hillock is 100 ft long by 70 ft. wide, roughly oval, and in it are a main winding shaft, the remains of a coe, an ore buddle, a climbing shaft and a horse-winding gin of which only the centre stone remains.

On top of the hillock lie the circle of the horse gin and its centre stone. The main shaft, to one side of the circle, is of an unusual 'D' shape 3 ft. across and 250 ft. deep. Below the west face of the hillock there is a terrace 25 ft. wide on which lie the ore-buddle and the coe, which is built into the hillside.

The coe itself is 8 ft. by 12 ft. with a partly paved stone floor and a fireplace with the chimney built into the thickness of the back wall. From one corner of the coe a passage 25 ft. long by 2 ft. 6 ins. high leads to a climbing shaft 33 ft. deep which descends to the south of the main shaft, allowing access to ¼ mile of workings with the aid of wire-ladders and ropes.

The buddle is floored at the top with sawn limestone slabs and lined with limestone blocks. A large gritstone slab across the foot of the first section has deep grooves on the top, probably from use as a whetstone. Below this slab a channel lined with limestone and wood leads to the edge of the terrace, above the settling dams.

The mine is on a number of scrins running east of north and seems to have been in its heyday in the mid 19th century. It was reported to be very productive in 1857 but in the period 1876-1883 the most productive year was 1879 when 9 tons 15 cwts. of ore was recovered.

It has been worked sporadically this century, the last known miner was Mr. Hodson of Grimsby, who worked the mine in the 1920s. A photograph taken in 1913 shows the horse-gin still standing but falling into ruin.

12. Stone Edge Cupola

2¼ ins.: 1 mile Map SK 36; 6 ins. 1 mile Map SK 36 NW. Grid Reference: SK 334.670.

Of all the smelting sites which have operated in Derbyshire, the Stone Edge Cupola, near the junction of the Ashover - Chesterfield (A632) and Darley Dale - Chesterfield (B6015) roads, is the most important and best preserved site. The cupola is scheduled as an Ancient Monument, whilst its chimney is the oldest free-standing industrial chimney in Britain, dating from about 1770 or even a little earlier; it is now listed in the Guinness Book of Records.

The site is on the high gritstone moorlands, to the east of the mining area of the limestone, and 2¼ miles north-west of Ashover at SK 334670, and is easily located by the tall square-built chimney at the centre of the site. This somewhat barren spot was chosen because the process gave off fumes and poisoned both vegetation and cattle. The two roads to the site, which are still known as Lead Lane and Belland (=lead poisoned) Lane, led from the formerly important lead-mining areas of Winster and Ashover, whilst Chesterfield was on the main lead-marketing route to Bawtry, Stockwith, and Hull, by road and later by canal.

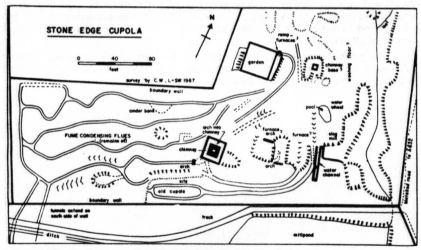

Plan of the Stone Edge Smelting works.

The cupola or reverberatory furnace was introduced to Derbyshire about 1735-37, almost simultaneously by the London Lead Company and by the Bagshawe and Twigg families. In this type of furnace the fuel, coal, was burned in a grate separated by a small wall or bridge from a saucer-shaped hearth in which the lead ore was placed, so as to avoid contamination. Flames from the fire 'reverberated' from the low arched roof of the furnace, causing the lead to separate from the waste or slag, and then passed via a flue to the tall chimney which provided the draught. The slag was

118

either raked or drawn off, whilst the lead was caused to run into a 'pot' at the front of the furnace. In the latter phases of the site's use, the flues were extended so as to cool and condense the lead 'fume' or vapour which came off with the gases. Unlike the ore-hearth which the cupola superseded, a bellows was not needed, but at Stone Edge there was also a slag mill, somewhat akin to a blacksmith's hearth, used to resmelt the cupola slag, so that the adjacent dam was built to provide water power for the bellows. The mill would probably be used at intervals, thus allowing the dam to fill again from the rather small catchment area.

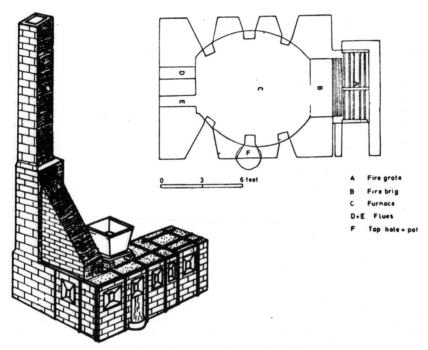

A	Fire grate	
B	Fire brig	
C	Furnace	
D+E	Flues	
F	Top hole + pot	

Plan and view of the Low Arched cupola at Stone Edge.

The features of the site still visible today show a complex situation owing to two, probably three, stages in the development of the works, during which the site of the furnaces was changed. The first reference to the site is for 1771 and, though the works were described by John Farey as rebuilt about 1811, the furnaces were still sited in a barn-like building just south of the tall chimney, where traces of an oblong platform can still be seen. Later furnaces, perhaps in the 1830's, were resited at a lower level, at which time the chimney was probably raised also, to provide increased draught when the flues were constructed. There appear to have been two furnaces east of the chimney, and one or two more close to the small enclosed garden, which must have been in use in the 1850's. At that date an entirely new process was introduced, probably the Spanish Slag Hearth, since the operator had recently

119

returned from Spain. (The new system was soon after introduced to Bradwell Slag Mill, see Itinerary 2). Three chimneys were used—one at the slag hearths near the water-works from the dam, one at the small garden probably to serve a roasting furnace of the cupola type to prepare ore for the Spanish Slag Hearth, and the main chimney which was served by a maze of flues, often running parallel, so as to slow the fumes down and encourage condensation. Entrances allowed access to permit the condensate to be removed to be resmelted. In the last period also, a steam engine was used for the draught, being required to operate the furnaces economically.

There are large quantities of furnace debris on the site. Furnaces were made of gritstone, lined with firebrick and sealed with fireclay and slag. Slags found are mainly greyish, but some appear rich in iron—but the absence of large heaps probably indicates the bulk of material was carted away, probably in the 1870's when Meerbrook Cupola specialised in slag treatment. Fume deposits can be found in the flues, whilst large quantities of cinder and ash are found over the flues to the west of the chimney.

The works were probably first built by Thornhill and Twigg, who had considerable interests at Ashover and Winster, including another cupola at Kelstedge, Ashover. For some time prior to 1789 the works was owned by John Twigg and Humphrey Winchester, whose business in that year failed, so that Twigg's Derbyshire and Welsh interests had to be hurriedly sold. It then passed into the hands of Barker and Wilkinson, who operated several cupolas in Derbyshire, and who produced up to 500 tons annually at Stone Edge, until in 1807 they moved their operations to their newly acquired works in Stoney Middleton. It was then occupied by Sykes, Milnes and Co. Milnes was a smelter who came from a long-established family of lead merchants in Ashover, whilst Sykes was head of one of Hull's best known shipping houses, presumably supplying both capital and market for the firm. In 1811 the works were described by John Farey as having the most improved cupolas in Derbyshire; Farey also gave a full account of the techniques of operation.

William and Charles Milnes appear to have used the site about the 1830's, but it was described as unused for about 15 years in 1849, except for a short while when a 'man named Pasco came from Cornwall'. Of Pasco nothing is known except that a Charles Pasco from Cornwall married a Sheldon girl, and lived at Sheldon in 1851, though at the time he was probably working away from home as a coal miner (he was probably one of the Cornish Magpie miners). Pasco stayed only a little while, but in 1848-9 the works were taken over by James Mitchel recently returned from Spain, who almost immediately became involved in a legal dispute over bellanding a horse. In Milnes' time the works had two cupolas and the water-powered slagmill, and whereas Milnes had paid for damage, Mitchel was reluctant. He had introduced two new slag mills, which usually resulted in increased pollution. References to horizontal flues suggest these were either then introduced, or possibly extended. A further legal suit over bellanding suggests that Mitchel may have remained at Stone Edge until about 1860, after which time the works probably became disused.

In 1875 the site was sold by the Reverend Nicholas Bourne Milnes to George Mowbrey, an ancestor of the present owners of the site, the Marriott family, though he reserved the right to remove the black slag, which, from its absence, he presumably did.

Visitors to the site should approach Mrs. Marriott of Spitewinter House, on the A632 road for permission.

13. Good Luck Mine, Via Gellia

2¼ inches : 1 mile Map SK 25; 6 inches : 1 mile Map SK 25 NE.

Situated on the south side of Via Gellia above the lay-by near the sharp bend above Marl Cottage (the unusual house built of large blocks of tufa), Good Luck Mine at SK 2700.5649 is a good example of small scale lead mining dating from the heyday of mining in the 1830's. The gated entrance is on top of the obvious spoil mound halfway up the hill slope. Hereabouts the hills overlooking the Via Gellia are cut by numerous lead veins, both parallel to and at right angles to the Cromford to Grangemill road, A5012. These veins were worked originally by shafts from the hill tops in the liberties of Cromford, Bonsall and Middleton. Later the same veins were approached by adits driven from the hillsides.

Goodluck is one of these. Originally the veins were worked by shafts each operated by separate small enterprises. One of these shafts was known as Goodluck Mine and was abandoned when the 'new turnpike' ran over it at the close of the 18th century. This 'new turnpike' was the steep road from Via Gellia to Middleton.

Other shaft workings were Bals Founder, Moore Jepson (now the site of Mountain Cottage, once the home of D. H. Lawrence about 1919) and Baker's Venture. Little is known of the early history of these mines but in 1783 one Gamaliel Hall fell down a turn in Goodluck Mine and was killed.

On 30th September 1830 these titles were consolidated and for the most part were acquired by John Alsop and Co., who were very active in the area at this time. It is recorded that this company, under the guidance of Roger Knowles—agent for the company, proposed to drive an adit from Middleton Wood to intersect the Goodluck Vein. On 26th October 1830 it is further recorded that work had begun, possibly the day before, which was a Monday.

The adit was driven by hand drilling and gunpowder blasting. The waste rock was tipped at the entrance resulting in the large spoil heap on the hillside.

The adit reached the vein after 97 fathoms. This probably took a year as a good driving rate was considered to be 90 fathoms per annum. The average cost at the time was £4 per fathom, so the total would be just under £400.

Whilst driving, other veins owned by other parties were cut. The first was Silver Eye Vein, part of the adjoining Silver Eye Title then owned by Isaac Spencer. An agreement was made that Spencer could use the adit for access to his vein if he paid one fifth of the cost of the driving. He also agreed not to remove waste rock through the adit. It can be seen where he backfilled this in the vein.

The second vein to be intersected was one of the Black Rakes, the owners here agreeing to pay 2 shillings (10p) per load of ore removed through the adit. They also agreed to sell their ore to John Alsop and Co. at the market value. The latter was a wise move by the agent as John Alsop owned the smelt in Bonsall Dale, the site now occupied by Cromford Garnetters. An eleven inch gauge tramway was laid for the use of the miners up the adit and into the vein.

Having reached Goodluck Vein it was worked by stoping upwards in the classical manner to a height varying from six to sixty feet. The waste rock (deads) were piled overhead on stone stemples. These latter are still in good condition and are one of the finest surviving examples of this lost art. At one point are the carved initials of the miners with the date Dec. 5th, 1831.

The vein was a poor one, galena representing on average 5% of the vein material with a gangue of baryte.

In several places the walls show thin beds of green clay, representing volcanic dust showers. The vein was worked up to the limit of the title, and in places it was worked below adit.

Having exhausted this vein, crosscuts were driven to intersect other veins. A good example of these is the crosscut known as the Gulph Gate which led them to four scrins: Else, Earl Grey, William IV and Godbers. The longest of these is Godbers, a vein very similar to Goodluck. Godbers Scrin cut through the only natural cave in the whole mine. Running water permitted some ore washing close to this rift.

The workings were later extended through a further crosscut branching south east at the end of Goodluck Vein, but these too were poor. The original shaft workings were broken into from time to time and some of these are accessible with difficulty. By the mid 1840's the mine was largely worked out and abandoned. It was worked sporadically for baryte; malachite, azurite and fluorspar sand were also found. The last attempt was in the 1950's, after which the adit entrance was blown in by the land owner.

The Peak District Mines Historical Society dug the entrance out, rendered it safe and gated it.

On the surface can be seen the coes for miners and ore dressers, as well as the powder house and dressing floor. These have also been excavated and preserved by the Society.

This mine represented a lot of hard work and capital investment for what appears to be small returns. Its value today is that a mine has been preserved having unspoilt features representative of lead mining. Access is limited to serious students of geology and mining history, by prior arrangement. Interested persons should contact the honorary secretary of the Peak District Mines Historical Society.

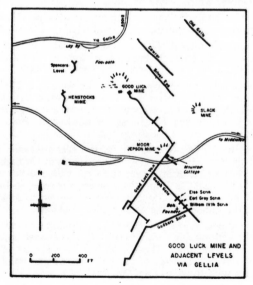

GOOD LUCK MINE AND ADJACENT LEVELS VIA GELLIA

Glossary

The terms listed below are the commonest of some 600 words, which are peculiar to the Derbyshire lead mining area, or which have special meanings there. The meanings given are the usual ones, but many had different shades of meaning in different parts of the area. A full list is given in *Derbyshire Lead Mining Glossary* by N. Kirkham, published by the Cave Research Group of Great Britain in 1949.

Adit — a horizontal tunnel into a mine from a hillside, often called a level, and sometimes functioning as a sough.

Adventurers — shareholders in a mine or sough.

Barmaster — the representative of the Crown, responsible for the administration of mining law, measuring ore, measuring out meers along a length of vein.

Barmote (= Barmoot) — the lead miners' court, usually held twice a year in each liberty, with a jury, once 24 in number, now 12, charged with judicial duties continuously from the sitting of one court until the next. The jury is called "The Body of the Mine".

Barytes — the mineral barium sulphate ($BaSO_4$); commonly called cawk, calk, caulk or heavy spar.

Basset — the outcrop of a vein or stratum.

Belland — finely powdered lead ore. It may cause poisoning in animals and men if allowed to flow into streams or on to grass. Animals so poisoned are said to be "belland(ed)".

Bing — large pieces of ore drawn from the mine and requiring little further dressing.

Black Jack — sulphide of zinc (ZnS), properly known as sphalerite. The chief ore of zinc.

Blende — the same as black jack.

Blue John — banded blue and white fluorspar, found only at Treak Cliff, Castleton.

Bole — a primitive smelting hearth, often on a hilltop, hence Bole Hill as a common place name.

Bouse — lead ore as raised from the mine before dressing.

Bucker — a broad, flat-headed hammer used mainly by women to break up ore to separate it from the gangue minerals.

Buddle — a wooden or stone trough or troughs used to wash light materials over baffles which catch the lead ore particles after crushing. To buddle is the act of so washing the ore.

Calcite — the mineral calcium carbonate ($CaCO_3$); sometimes worked as a calc-spar for decorative or building purposes.

Calk, caulk, or cawk — barytes, barium sulphate, also known as heavy spar. The chief source of barium chemicals in industry.

Calamine	—zinc carbonate (ZnCO₃), the cream-coloured oxidation mineral resulting from the weathering of blende, often known as "dry-bone". Used in cosmetics, medicine and formerly in the manufacture of brass.
Cat Dirt	—decomposed toadstone, weathered basalt lava.
Channel	—decomposed toadstone.
Cheeks	—the sides or walls of a vein.
Chert	—a hard siliceous rock, like flint, found as nodules and layers in the limestone. Often black, but may weather white. It may replace limestone with enclosed fossil crinoids and is then known as 'screwstone'.
Coe	—a small shed, usually of stone, above or near a mine, in which the miners kept their tools, and sometimes a change of clothing. The climbing shaft was often under a trap door in the floor of the coe.
Cope	—a duty paid by miners to the Lord, by virtue of which they may sell their ore to whom they wish, and which may be a fixed price per load paid by the miners by agreement with the mine agent.
Corfe or Corve	—a crude wooden sledge used to convey ore, etc. underground, sometimes along wooden rails.
Cross-cut	—a passage cut through solid rock from one vein to another.
Cupola	—a reverberatory furnace for smelting lead ore.
Deads	—useless stone from a vein or working, usually stacked in abandoned workings, often on timber platforms which are now dangerously unstable.
Dial	—a miners' compass used in surveying underground.
Dish	—the measure for lead ore, either oblong or circular, varying from liberty to liberty, but generally holding between 14 and 15 Winchester pints. Nine dishes=one load; one dish=about 65 lbs.; approximately 3½-4 loads=1 ton. A standard dish made in 1512 is kept at the Moot Hall, Wirksworth.
Dolomite	—the mineral, or the rock composed dominantly of it, calcium magnesium carbonate (CaMg (CO₃)₂). Outcrops chiefly around Brassington and Elton. Sometimes used as a source of refractory brick material, or as a source of magnesium metal.
Dunstone	—generally applied to dolomite rock, but has been applied to toadstone, or to ironstone in different areas.
Egg and Eye	—the notch and slot made in opposite walls of a vein to hold a stemple or wooden beam.
Engine	—applied to any winding or pumping machinery, whether worked by hand, horse or steam.
Engine-shaft	—a larger shaft equipped with winding machinery rather than a stowes (windlass).

Fangs	—wood or metal pipes used to convey fresh air to the workings
Fathom	—a measure of 6 feet, commonly used to express the depth of mines and shafts.
Fissures	—cracks or joints in the rocks, either open or filled with loose stones.
Firing	—fire-setting—the practice before the days of explosives, of lighting a fire against the face of the vein to open cracks, and make it more easy to extract the lead ore. By law it could only be done after 4 p.m.
Flat	—a body of ore generally lying more or less horizontally, of equal length and width, usually parallel with the stratification of the enclosing limestone. By elongation flats grade into pipes.
Fluorspar	—the mineral fluorite, calcium fluoride (CaF_2), widely used as a flux in blast furnaces and as a source of fluorine in chemical industry. Also used for special glasses and ceramics.
Forefield	—the working face of a mine, usually the furthest point from the shaft.
Fother	—a measure of lead, normally by volume, occasionally in recent times by weight, in both cases varying from liberty to liberty, ranging from 1,680 lbs. to 2,520 lbs., usually nearer the latter.
Founder	—the first miner to work a mine; or the first meers allocated by the barmaster to found the mine; or the first shaft sunk.
Freeing	—the act of delivering to the barmaster a dish of ore to establish ownership of a new vein or mine.
Galena	—the mineral lead sulphide (PbS). The chief ore of lead.
Gang, or Gangue	—the waste minerals found with the lead ore, usually dumped on the hillock. Since the minerals include fluorspar and barytes, they are now often more valuable than the lead and many hillocks have been reprocessed for the gangue.
Gate	—a way or passage in a mine; an access route.
Gin	—a winding engine; a horse-gin, driven by horses; also known as a whim.
Gin circle	—the circular area, round which the horse plodded to work the gin.
Ginging	—the dressed stonework around the top parts of a shaft holding up the loose ground.
Grove or Groove	—a mine; sometimes applied to a length of vein being worked more or less as a single mine; sometimes restricted to open workings at the surface.
Hade	—the slope of a vein from the vertical.
Heading	—alternative name for a cross-cut, gate or adit.
Hillocks, hillocking	—old tip heaps, searching them for unrecovered minerals.

Icles, water-icicles, watricle	—stalactites, as found in caves.
Jagger	—one who carries lead ore from the mines to the smelting place on pack-horses.
Jig	—a concentrating device used to separate the lead ore from the gangue.
Kebble, Kibble	—a large bucket used to lift the ore up the shaft.
Level	—a horizontal tunnel, adit, sough or gate. A level may also be a surveying instrument.
Liberty	—the district in which the miner searches for ore. Derbyshire has several liberties with slightly differing laws and customs.
Load .	—a measure of lead ore, being 9 dishes, varying between 3½ and 4 loads to a ton.
Lord	—the owner of the mineral liberty, who receives the "lot", and usually also the "cope".
Lord's Meer	—a length of vein laid out by the barmaster for the lord, who receives all the ore obtained from it, or makes special arrangements with the miners.
Lot	—the share of ore to the lord, usually every 13th dish, though he may take anything from the 10th to the 25th according to the Liberty and other circumstances, measured at reckonings every 6 weeks or so.
Marble	—in the geological sense it is strictly a limestone which has been recrystallized by the subsequent application of heat and pressure. Commercially the term "marble" is applied to any limestone which will take a polish.
Meer	—a measure of length of a vein, varying in different liberties, 27, 28, 29, 30 or 32 yards. Two founder meers are usually allocated to the discoverers of a vein. Taker meers are added later. Lord's Meer is the one allocated to the lord, usually next to the founder meers.
Mine Royal	—a mine containing gold or silver to a value greater than that of the associated base metals.
Nicking	—failure to work a mine may allow another miner to claim it, by asking the barmaster to "nick", i.e. cut a piece out of, the stowes. Three nickings allow the mine to be forfeited and handed over to the claimant, unless excess water or lack of ventilation prevent the mine being worked.
Offal	—waste, gangue and rock, sometimes including unrecoverable lead ore.
Old Man	—(t'owd man) places worked by former miners; or the former miners themselves.
Open	—a naturally open cavern or fissure.
Ore	—the valuable mineral from which a metal can be extracted. In Derbyshire it refers only to lead ore, galena.

Pig	—the block of cast lead metal in the smelter's works. Commonly 8 pigs make one fother.
Pipe	—a body of ore lying more or less horizontally, but long and narrow. Grades into a flat by broadening. Many pipe-veins are in fact ancient caverns filled with ore and gangue. Pipes may branch out of rakes.
Quarter Cord	—ground allowed to the miner either side of a vein to deposit his refuse and build his coe, a quarter of a meer in width.
Rake	—the main type of mineral vein in the Peak District. A body of ore and gangue minerals disposed vertically between two walls of rock, and thus having a straight course across country. Rakes may be up to several miles long, but grade in size down into scrins, which are, broadly speaking, small rakes.
Rider	—a mass of rock dividing a vein. Also known as a horse.
Rise	—an underground shaft driven upwards above a working.
Scrin	—a short, often thin, vertical vein of ore; often branching out of a rake.
Self-open	—a large natural cavern.
Shack	—a natural opening in the ground; also known as a shake, or shake-hole, sometimes filled with loose rocks.
Shale-gate	—a tunnel cut through shale.
Sinkers	—the men who make shafts.
Slag	—the waste material produced during smelting lead ore.
Slickensides	—the shiny, grooved surfaces produced by movements of the strata along geological faults. Sometimes still in a state of stress, and liable to explode on being disturbed by mining.
Smelting	—extracting the lead metal from the ore.
Smitham	—finely powdered ore produced by the crusher.
Sole	—the floor of a mine or sough; the lowest level worked.
Sough	—an adit or tunnel driven specifically to drain a mine.
Soughers	—those who dig soughs.
Spar	—a collective term for the crystalline minerals found with lead-ore; variously applied to fluorspar, barytes (heavy spar), calcite, (calc-spar).
Stemple	—a piece of wood wedged across a working or vein, for use as a rung of a climbing way, or as part of a platform or lodgement for stacking deads, or part of a roof support. Stemples of dressed stone occur in a few mines.
Steward	—the presiding officer of the Barmote Court. The lord's executive.
Stope	—a worked-out vein left as an open cavity.
Stowes (stoes, stoce)	—the wooden windlass over a shaft for raising ore. The stowes had to be made to a definite pattern, and the existence of a pair of stowes (i.e. one windlass) was a symbol of ownership of a mine.

Strike	—the course or direction of a vein or stratum.
Sump	—any vertical opening in a mine not connecting to the surface; an internal shaft; sometimes called a winze or turn. Alternatively a sump is a hollow in the bottom of a mine for collecting the drainage before pumping.
Swallow or Swallet	—a natural opening which takes water away.
Tailings	—the finely ground waste from a modern ore-processing plant.
Toadstone	—a collective name for several types of basaltic volcanic rock. It may be compact basalt, or may have vesicles (gas-bubble cavities), or may be decomposed to a green clay, or may be rubbly volcanic ash.
Turn	—an underground shaft, also called a sump or a winze.
Turntree	—alternative term for a stowes.
The Twenty-four	—the Grand Jury of the Barmote Court, the "Body of the Mine".
Vein	—the body of minerals enclosed by rock.
Vein-stuff	—the minerals, etc. in a vein.
Wad	—impure manganese ore, a mixture of iron and manganese oxides.
Water-gate	—a sough or drainage level.
Water-icicles, watricles	—stalactites.
Way-board	—a clay bed between beds of limestone, usually not more than a few inches thick.
Wheat-ore, White ore	—lead carbonate, the mineral cerussite ($PbCO_3$). Worked as an ore, often used in lead paints.
Whim	—a winding engine worked by horses or steam.
Whimsey	—a steam-driven winding engine.
Winze	—a small underground shaft sunk from one part of a mine to another.
Woughs	—the limestone walls of a vein.

ACKNOWLEDGMENTS

This book could not have been compiled without the co-operation of many people in whose care there are collections of manuscripts concerned with lead-mining. In particular the authors would like to express their gratitude to the following:-

The Trustees of the Chatsworth Settlement for access to the Devonshire Collections at Chatsworth House.

The Director of the Manuscript Collection in the British Museum Library for help with the Woolley Manuscripts.

The Librarian of the Local History Department, Sheffield City Libraries, for access to the Bagshawe Collection, Oakes Deeds and Wager Holmes collection.

Miss Lees of the Derbyshire County Library for access to manuscripts.

Miss J. Sinar of the Derbyshire Record Office for access to the Brooke-Taylor documents and many others.

The late Mr. John Mort, Barmaster, and his successor Mr. W. M. Erskine, for access to the Barmaster's Books.

Mr. B. Miller of Bagshawe, Miller & Co., Solicitors, Sheffield, for the gift of the Bagshawe-Manton documents from their office to J. Rieuwerts.

Mr. and Mrs. Marriott, Mr. M. Brooke-Taylor and the late Mr. R. W. P. Cockerton, for access to private documents.

The editors and authors would like to acknowledge their indebtedness to the late Miss Nellie Kirkham for her help and encouragement of all interested in the old lead mines. Without her pioneer works in this field it is doubtful if this book could have been written. We thank Don Aldridge, formerly of the Peak Park Planning Board, for designing this guide book, and Mrs. Nita Farquharson for drawing most of the maps. The Whitworth Art Gallery, Manchester, have kindly allowed us to use a photograph of John Webber's painting of Odin Mine. Other photographs have been kindly supplied by the Derbyshire Pennine Club, Laporte Industries Ltd., Glebe Mines, Eyam, and by Messrs. H. M. Parker, F. Nixon, the late F. Brindley and R. Thornhill. Mr. H. E. Chatburn kindly allowed us to use his site plans of mines near Castleton. The Midland Institute of Mining Engineers have kindly allowed us to reproduce some of A. H. Stokes' drawings from their Transactions of 1880. Others whose help has been invaluable include J. Beck, N. J. D. Butcher, R. Flindall, A. Greenwood, L. Gregory, T. Hodson, D. Manton, B. Marshall, the late C. H. Millington, Miss A. Pennial, Dr. W. A. S. Sarjeant and B. Webster.

Select Bibliography

AGRICOLA, G., 1556. "De Re Metallica". (English translation by H. & L. Hoover, 1912). Dover Press.

ANON., 1961. "Quarrying Limestone Underground (at Middleton-by-Wirksworth)". Mine & Quarry Eng. Vol. 26, pp. 344-352.

BROWN, I. J., 1966. "End of an Era". Bull. Peak Dist. Mines Hist. Soc., Vol. 3, pt. 2, pp. 75-84.

CARRUTHERS, R. G. & STRAHAN, A. 1923. "Lead and Zinc Ores of Durham, Yorkshire and Derbyshire with notes on the Isle of Man". Geol. Surv. Spec. Rep. Min. Res. Vol. 26, pp. 41-88.

COPE, F. W. 1965. "The Peak District". Guide No. 26. Geologists Assoc. 27p.

DONALD, M. B. 1961. "Elizabethan Monopolies".

DUNHAM, K. C. 1952. "Fluorspar". Geol. Surv. Spec. Rep. Min. Res., Vol. 4, 4th edition, 143p.

DRURY, G. H. 1963. "The East Midlands and the Peak". Nelson, London.

EDWARDS, K. C. 1962. "The Peak District". Collins New Naturalist, London.

FAREY, J. 1811. "A General View of the Agriculture and Minerals of Derbyshire". Vol. 1. 532p.

FORD, T. D. 1961. "Recent Studies of Mineral Distribution in Derbyshire and their Significance". Bull. Peak Dist. Mines Hist. Soc., Vol. 1, pt. 5, pp. 3-9.

FORD, T. D. 1967. "The Caves of Derbyshire". 2nd Edn. Dalesman Press. 144p.

FORD, T. D. 1969. "The Stratiform Ore Deposits of Derbyshire". pp. 73-96. in Proc. 15th Inter-University Geological Congress, Leicester.

FORD, T. D. 1967. "Some Mineral Deposits of the Carboniferous Limestone of Derbyshire". pp. 53-75, in Geological Excursions in the Sheffield Area and the Peak District National Park, edited by R. Neves & C. Downie, University of Sheffield.

FORD, T. D. & INESON, P. R. 1971. "The Fluorspar mining potential of the Derbyshire Orefield". Trans. Inst. Mining & Metallurgy. Vol. B80, pp. 186-210.

FORD, T. D. & MASON, M. H. 1967. "Bibliography of the Geology of the Peak District of Derbyshire up to 1965". Mercian Geol. Vol. 2, No. 2, pp. 133-244. Supplement in Vol. 4, No. 2, 1972.

FORD, T. D. & SARJEANT, W. A. S. 1964. "The Peak District Mineral Index". Bull. Peak Dist. Mines Hist. Soc., Vol. 2, pp. 122-150.

FULLER, J. M. 1965. "Lead Mining in Derbyshire in the mid-nineteenth Century". East Midland Geog., Vol. 3, No. 7, pp. 373-393.

GLOVER, S. 1829. "History and Gazetteer of the County of Derby". 2 Vols.

GREEN, A. H. et al. 1887. "The Geology of the Carboniferous Limestone, Yoredale Rocks and Millstone Grit of North Derbyshire". 2nd edn., Mem. Geol. Surv.

HARDY, W. 1714. "The Miners' Guide".

HARRIS, H. 1971. "Industrial Archaeology of the Peak District". David & Charles, Newton Abbot.

HOLMES, J. F. 1962. "Lead Mining in Derbyshire". Mining Mag., Vol. 107, pp. 137-148.

HOPKINSON, G. G. 1958. "Five Generations of Derbyshire Lead Mining and Smelting". Derbys. Arch. Jour., Vol. 78, pp. 9-24.

KIRKHAM, N. 1950. "Old Drowned Work in Derbyshire". Derbys. Arch. Jour., Vol. 70, pp. 1-20.

KIRKHAM, N. 1953. "The Tumultuous Course of Dovegang". Derbys. Arch. Jour., Vol. 73, pp. 1-35.

KIRKHAM, N. 1960-61. "The Draining of the Alport Mines". Trans. Newcomen Soc., Vol. 33, pp. 67-91.

KIRKHAM, N. 1961. "Winster Sough". Bull. Peak Dist. Mines Hist. Soc., Vol. 1, No. 5, pp 10-29.

KIRKHAM, N. 1964-6. "Eyam Edge Mines and Soughs". Bull. Peak Dist. Mines Hist. Soc., Vol. 2, pp. 241-254 and 315-334; Vol. 3, pp. 43-57 and 130-118.

KIRKHAM, N. 1965-66. "Steam Engines in Derbyshire's Lead Mines". Trans. Newcomen Soc., Vol. 38.

KIRKHAM, N. 1968. "Derbyshire Lead Mining through the Centuries". Bradford Barton, Truro.

MANLOVE, E. 1653. "The Liberties and Customs of the Lead Mines within the Wapentake of Wirksworth in the County of Derby". Composed in Meter. (Reprinted in A. H. Stokes, 1880).

NEVES, R. & DOWNIE, C. 1967. "Geological Excursions in the Sheffield Region and the Peak District National Park". University of Sheffield. 163p.

NIXON, F. 1957-9. "The Early Steam Engine in Derbyshire". Trans. Newcomen Soc., Vol. 31, 28p.

NIXON, F. 1969. "The Industrial Archaeology of Derbyshire". David and Charles, Newton Abbot.

O'NEAL, R. 1961. "A Bibliography of Derbyshire Lead Mining". Derbyshire County Library.

PERCY, J. 1870. "The Metallurgy of Lead". Murray, London.

RAISTRICK, A. & JENNINGS, B. 1965. "A History of Lead Mining in the Pennines". Longmans, London.

RIEUWERTS, J. H. 1963. "Lathkilldale: Its Mines and Miners". Bull. Peak Dist. Mines Hist. Soc., Vol. 2, No. 1, pp. 9-30.

RIEUWERTS, J. H. 1966. "A List of the Soughs of the Derbyshire Lead Mines". Bull. Peak Dist. Mines Hist. Soc., Vol. 3, No. 1, pp. 1-42. (Supplementary list in Vol. 4, No. 2), 1969.

RIEUWERTS, J. H. 1972. "Derbyshire's Old Lead Mines and Miners". Moorlands Publ. Co., Hartington.

ROBEY, J. A. & PORTER, L. 1972. "The Copper and Lead Mines of Ecton Hill, Staffordshire". Moorlands Publ. Co., Hartington.

SMITH, E. G., RHYS, G. H., & EDEN, R. A. 1967. "Geology of the Country Around Chesterfield, Matlock and Mansfield". Mem. Geol. Surv., 430p.

STOKES, A. H. 1880-1882. "Lead and Lead-mining in Derbyshire". Trans. Chesterfield & Derbys. Inst. Min. Civ. Mech. Eng. (reprinted 1973 as Peak Dist. Mines Hist. Soc. Spec. Pub. No. 2).

STEVENSON, I. P. & GAUNT, G. D. 1971. "Geology of the Country Around Chapel-en-le-Frith (and Castleton)". Inst. Geol. Sciences, London (H.M.S.O.).

STRAHAN, A. 1887. "On Explosive Slickensides". Geol. Mag. Dec. 3. Vol. 4, pp. 400-408.

SYLVESTER-BRADLEY, P. C. & FORD, T. D. 1968. "Geology of the East Midlands". Univ. Leicester Press, 400p.

TAYLOR, L. F. 1958. "Mill Close Mine". Derbyshire Countryside.

VARVILL, W. W. 1959. "The Future of Lead-Zinc and Fluorspar Mining in Derbyshire". In Symposium on the Future of Non-ferrous Mining in Great Britain. Inst. Min. Met., pp. 175-232.

VARVILL, W. W. 1962. "Secondary Enrichment by Natural Flotation". Mine and Quarry Eng. Vol. 27, pp. 64-73, 112-118, 156-161, 208-214.

WILLIES, L. 1971. "The Introduction of the Cupola to Derbyshire". Bull. Peak Dist. Mines Hist. Soc., Vol. 4, pp. 384-394.

WILLIES, L. 1969. "Cupola Lead Smelting Sites in Derbyshire, 1737-1900". Bull. Peak Dist. Mines Hist. Soc., Vol. 4, pp. 97-115.

Additional References for the Itineraries

1. Castleton

FORD, T. D. 1954. "Treak Cliff Cavern". Trans. Cave Res. Group G.B., Vol. 3, No. 2, pp. 125-135.

FORD, T. D. 1955. "Blue John Fluorspar". Proc. Yorks. Geol. Soc., Vol. 30, pp. 35-60.

FORD, T. D. 1956. "The Speedwell Mine". Trans. Cave Res. Group G.B., Vol. 4, No. 2, pp. 99-124.

2. Bradwell

CRABTREE, P. W. 1965. "Notes on the Bradwell Caverns, Part II; Lead Smelting at Bradwell". Cave Science, Vol. 5, No. 38, pp. 331-338.

EVANS, S. 1912. "Bradwell Ancient and Modern". Chesterfield, 135 pp.

3. Eyam and Stoney Middleton

ANON. 1965. "The Cavendish Mill (and Glebe Mines)". Minerals & Mining Eng., Vol. 1, No. 15, pp. 579-586.

ANON. 1968. "Mining at Sallet Hole", Minerals and Mining Eng, Vol. 4, No. 3, pp. 105-106.

ANON. 1965. "Fluorspar Flotation at Glebe Mines". Mining Mag., Vol. 113, pp. 276-283.

KIRKHAM, N. 1964-6. "Eyam Edge Mines and Soughs". Bull. Peak Dist. Mines Hist. Soc., Vol. 2, pp. 241-254, 315, 335; Vol. 3, pp. 43-57, 103-118.

KIRKHAM, N. 1966. "Longstone Edge Mines and Soughs". Part 1. Cave Science. Vol. 5, No. 39, pp. 354-368; Part 2, Cave Science, Vol. 6, No. 40, pp. 440-469.

WILLIES, L. 1974. "The Lords Cupola, Stoney Middleton". Bull. Peak Dist. Mines Hist. Soc., Vol. 5, pp. 288-301.

4. Magpie Mine & Sheldon

ANON. 1955. "Don't Go Down the Mine". Iron & Coal Trades Review. Vol. 171, pp. 13-14.

BROWN, I. J. & FORD, T. D. 1971. "Magpie Mine, Sheldon". Peak Dist. Mines Hist. Soc. Spec. Pub. No. 3 (3rd edition).

KIRKHAM, N. 1960. "Magpie Mine and Sough". Sorby Record, Vol. 1, No. 3, pp. 31-39.

KIRKHAM, N. 1963. "Magpie Mine and Its Tragedy". Derbyshire Miscellany, Vol. 2, No. 8, pp. 359-382.

MATTHEWS, J. 1960. "Magpie Mine and Sough". Bull. Peak Dist. Mines Hist. Soc., Vol. 1, No. 3, pp. 13-15.

ROBEY, J. A. 1966. "Fieldgrove Mine". Bull. Peak Dist. Mines Hist. Soc., Vol. 3, pp. 93-101.

WILLIES, L. 1974. "The Re-opening of the Magpie Sough". Bull. Peak Dist. Mines Hist. Soc., Vol. 5, pp. 324-331.

5. Ashford Black Marble Mines

FORD, T. D. 1958. "The Black Marble of Ashford-in-the-Water". Liverpool & Manchester Geol. Jour., Vol. 2, pp. 44-59.

FORD, T. D. 1964. "The Black Marble Mines of Ashford-in-the-Water". Bull. Peak Dist. Mines Hist. Soc., Vol. 2, No. 4, pp. 179-188.

6. Lathkilldale

RIEUWERTS, J. H. 1963. "Lathkilldale: Its Mines and Miners". Bull. Peak Dist. Mines Hist. Soc., Vol. 2, pp. 9-30.

RIEUWERTS, J. H. 1973. "Lathkill Dale : Its Mines and Miners". Moorlands Publ. Co., Hartington.

TUNE, R. 1969. "A Survey of Mandale Mine". Bull. Peak Dist. Mines Hist. Soc., Vol. 4, No. 1, pp. 67-74.

7. Monyash Mines

KITCHEN, G. & PENNEY, D. 1973. "New Pumps for Old". Bull. Peak Dist. Mines Hist. Soc., Vol. 5, pp. 129-136.

ROBEY, J. A. 1961-63. "The Mines North-west of Monyash, Parts 1-3". Bull. Peak Dist. Mines Hist. Soc., Vol. 1, No. 5, pp. 30-36; Vol. 1, No. 6, pp. 29-32; Vol. 2, No. 1, pp. 51-56.

ROBEY, J. A. 1965. "The Drainage of the Area Between the Rivers Wye and Lathkill". Proc. Brit. Speleo. Assoc., No. 3, pp.1-10.

ROBEY, J. A. 1973. "Supplementary Notes on the Monyash-Flagg Area". Bull. Peak Dist. Mines Hist. Soc., Vol. 5, pp. 149-155.

8. Alport

KIRKHAM, N. 1960-61. "The Drainage of the Alport Mines". Trans. Newcomen Soc., Vol. 33, pp. 67-91.

KIRKHAM, N. 1965-66. "Steam Engines in Derbyshire's Lead Mines". Trans. Newcomen Soc., Vol. 38, pp. 69-88.

KIRKHAM, N. 1964-65. "The Ventilation of Hillcarr Sough". Trans. Newcomen Soc., Vol. 37, pp. 133-138.

KIRKHAM, N. 1964. "Wheels Rake, Alport-by-Youlgreave". Bull. Peak Dist. Mines Hist. Soc., Vol. 2, Part 3, pp. 153-173.

(The Authors wish to express their indebtedness to these articles by Miss Nellie Kirkham, particularly those in the Transactions of the Newcomen Society, for the inspiration they provided in studies of this area).

9. Matlock and Cromford

BRYAN, B. 1903. "Matlock Manor and Parish". Historical and descriptive.

FLINDALL, R. & HAYES, A. 1972. "Wapping Mine and Cumberland Cavern, Matlock Bath". Bull. Peak Dist. Mines Hist. Soc., Vol. 5, pp. 114-127.

FLINDALL, R. & HAYES, A. 1973. "The Mines near Upperwood—the Tear Breeches-Hopping-Fluorspar-Speedwell complex". Bull. Peak Dist. Mines Hist. Soc., Vol. 5, pp. 182-199.

HURT, L. 1970. "A Survey of Ball Eye Mines, Bonsall". Bull. Peak Dist. Mines Hist. Soc., Vol. 4, pp. 289-305.

KIRKHAM, N. 1963. "Old Mill Close Lead Mine". Bull. Peak Dist. Mines Hist. Soc., Vol. 2, No. 1, pp. 70-82.

KIRKHAM, N. 1963. "The Draining of Wirksworth Lead Mines". Derbyshire Arch. Soc. Local Hist. Sect., 19 pp.

RAISTRICK, A. 1937. "Mill Close Mine in Derbyshire". Proc. Univ. Durham Phil. Soc., Vol. 10, pp. 38-47.

TRAILL, J. G. 1939. "The Geology and Development of Mill Close Mine". Econ. Geol., Vol. 34, pp. 851-889.

VARVILL, W. W. 1937. "A Study of the Shapes and Distribution of Lead Deposits in the Pennines". Trans. Inst. Min. Met., Vol. 46, pp. 463-559.

VARVILL, W. W. 1962. "Secondary Enrichment by Natural Flotation". Mine & Quarry Eng., Vol. 27, pp. 64-73, 112-118, 156-161, 208-214.

10. Crich

BEMROSE, H. H. ARNOLD. 1894. "Notes on Crich Hill". Derbys. Arch. Jour., Vol. 16, pp. 44-51.

GREGORY, N. 1966. "Notes and Impressions of Jingler Mine, Wakebridge". Bull. Peak Dist. Mines Hist., Soc. Vol. 3, pp. 58-62.

KIRKHAM, N. 1957. "Ridgeway Level, Whatstandwell". Derbyshire Miscellany, Vol. 1, No. 6, pp. 72-75.

KIRKHAM, N. 1969. "Lead Mining at Crich". Manchester Assoc. of Eng. Prov. 113th session, No. 5, 17 pp.

11. Carsington Pastures

FORD, T. D. & KING, R. J. 1965. "Layered Epigenetic Galena-barite Deposits in the Golconda Mine, Brassington". Econ. Geol., Vol. 60, pp. 1686-1701.

FORD, T. D. & KING, R. J. 1966. "The Golconda Caverns". Trans. Cave Research Group G.B., Vol. 7, No. 2, pp. 91-114.

FORD, T. D. & KING, R. J. 1969. "The Origin of the Silica Sand Deposits of the Derbyshire Limestone". Mercian Geol., Vol. 3, pp. 51-70.

GREGORY, N. & TUNE, R. 1967. "Ore Buddles at Snake Mine, Hopton, and at Bonsall Leys". Bull. Peak Dist. Mines Hist. Soc., Vol. 3, pp. 253-255.

TUNE, R., HURT, L. & FORD, T. D. 1968. "Snake Mine, Hopton". Bull. Peak Dist. Mines Hist. Soc., Vol. 3, No. 5, pp. 291-298.

YORKE, COURTENAY. 1961. "The Pocket Deposits of Derbyshire". Birkenhead. (Private Publication).

12. Stone Edge Cupola

WILLIAMS, C. J. & WILLIES, L. 1968. "Stone Edge Cupola". Bull. Peak Dist. Mines Hist. Soc., Vol. 3, pp. 315-322.

WILLIES, L. 1969. "Cupola Lead-smelting Sites in Derbyshire. 1737-1900". Bull. Peak Dist. Mines Hist. Soc., Vol. 4, No. 1, pp. 97-115.

WILLIES, L. 1972. "Gabriel Jars (1732-1769) and the Derbyshire Lead Industry". Bull. Peak Dist. Mines Hist. Soc., Vol. 5, pp. 31-39.

13. Good Luck Mine, Via Gellia

WILLIES, L. 1969, "Cupola Lead Smelting Sites in Derbyshire 1737-1900". Bulletin P.D.M.H.S. Vol. 4, part 1, pp 97-115.

FLINDALL, R. & HAYES, A. 1972, "A Survey of Goodluck Mine and Adjacent Levels in the Via Gellia". Bull. P.D.M.H.S., Vol. 5, part 1, pp. 61-80.

AMNER, R. & NAYLOR, P. 1973, "Goodluck Mine, Via Gellia". Bull. P.D.M.H.S., Vol. 5, part 4, pp 217-240.

THE BULLETIN OF THE PEAK DISTRICT MINES HISTORICAL SOCIETY

The BULLETIN, first published in 1959, is issued twice yearly without charge to paid-up members of the Society – non-members wishing to buy copies should contact the Secretary at the address below.

Volume 1 was published in 7 parts (1959-1962); all subsequent volumes are in 6 parts; volume 5 was completed in 1974. Many parts are still available from M. Luff, 14 Tredington Road, Glenfield, Leicester. Prices on request.

Enquiries concerning membership and subscriptions should be sent to the Secretary, P.D.M.H.S., The Mining Museum, The Pavilion, Matlock Bath, Derbyshire.

From time to time the Society publishes SPECIAL PUBLICATIONS which are charged separately to members and non-members alike, for example:

"The History of Magpie Mine, Sheldon" by L. N. Willies and others, 4th Edn., 1980 – obtainable from the Mining Museum.

Printed in England.

Arthur Gaunt and Sons (Printers) Limited, 14 Godfrey Street, Heanor, Derbyshire.